D1321470

GEOLOGICAL CONSERVATION
REVIEW SERIES No. 1

An Introduction to the *Geological Conservation Review*

N. V. Ellis (Editor)

D. Q. Bowen

S. Campbell

J. L. Knill

A. P. McKirdy

C. D. Prosser

M. A. Vincent

R. C. L. Wilson

JOINT NATURE CONSERVATION COMMITTEE

CYNGOR CEFN GWLAD CYMRU

COUNTRYSIDE COUNCIL FOR WALES

ENGLISH NATURE

SCOTTISH NATURAL HERITAGE

Published by the Joint Nature Conservation Committee
Monkstone House
City Road
Peterborough
PE1 1JY

First edition 1996

© 1996 Joint Nature Conservation Committee

ISBN 1 86107 403 4

British Library Cataloguing-in-Publication Data

A catalogue record for this book is available from the British Library.

Recommended citation for this volume:
Ellis, N.V. (ed.), Bowen, D.Q., Campbell, S., Knill, J.L., McKirdy, A.P., Prosser, C.D., Vincent, M.A. and Wilson, R.C.L. (1996) *An Introduction to the Geological Conservation Review*. GCR Series No. 1, Joint Nature Conservation Committee, Peterborough.

British Geological Survey copyright protected materials

1. The copyright of materials derived from the British Geological Survey's work is vested in the Natural Environment Research Council. No part of these materials (geological maps, charts, plans, diagrams, graphs, cross-sections, figures, sketch maps, tables, photographs) may be reproduced or transmitted in any form or by any means, or stored in a retrieval system of any nature, without the written permission of the copyright holder, in advance.

2. To ensure that copyright infringements do not arise, permission has to be obtained from the copyright owner. In the case of BGS maps this includes **both BGS and Ordnance Survey**. Most BGS geological maps make use of Ordnance Survey topography (Crown Copyright), and this is acknowledged on BGS maps. Reproduction of Ordnance Survey materials may be independently permitted by the licences issued by Ordnance Survey to many users. Users who do not have an Ordnance Survey licence to reproduce the topography must make their own arrangements with the Ordnance Survey, Copyright Branch, Romsey Road, Southampton SO9 4DH (Tel. 01703 792913).

3. Permission to reproduce BGS materials must be sought in writing from Dr Jean Alexander, Copyright Manager, British Geological Survey, Kingsley Dunham Centre, Keyworth, Nottingham NG12 5GG (Tel. 0115 936 3331).

Page layout and design by: R & W Publications (Newmarket) Ltd
Printed in Great Britain by: Halstan & Co Limited, Amersham, Buckinghamshire

Contents

Contents

Contents

v

Acknowledgements

The Joint Nature Conservation Committee wishes to acknowledge the contribution made by the late Chris Stevens. His guidance and enthusiasm provided a valuable impetus during the early stages of text writing. Thanks go to those individuals who have written text and made editorial contributions to this volume: Dr P. H. Banham, Mr J. H. Bratton, Dr K. L. Duff, Dr J. L. Eyers, Dr N. F. Glasser, Dr J. E. Gordon, Dr J. G. Larwood, Dr R. G. Lees, Professor J. McManus, Dr T. Moat, Dr D. P. A. O'Halloran, Dr K. N. Page, Dr L. P. Thomas, Mr D. A. White, Dr W. A. Wimbledon and Ms F. J. Wright.

The help of the consultees to the draft of the volume is gratefully acknowledged. Those who commented are too numerous to mention individually, but their contributions proved invaluable in the preparation of the final typescript.

Foreword

In the rocks and landscapes of Britain lies the evidence for ancient events which fashioned the small but complex part of the Earth's crust that we now call the British Isles. By piecing together this evidence, it is possible to construct the geological history of Britain. Magnus Magnusson, the Chairman of Scottish Natural Heritage and one of my colleagues on the Joint Nature Conservation Committee, said that:

> 'Our geological past involves a barely believable story of whole continents moving around like croutons floating on a bowl of thick soup, of great oceans forming and disappearing like seasonal puddles, of mighty mountains being thrown up and worn down, of formidable glaciers and ice caps advancing and retreating behind mile-thick walls of ice as they melted and reformed again. Scotland has been a desert, a tropical rain forest and a desert again; it has drifted north over the planet with an ever-changing cargo of lizards, dinosaurs, tropical forests, giant redwoods, sharks, bears, lynx, giant elk, wolves and also human beings.

> 'There is a fascinating story to tell that is of profound relevance to the world.'

What Magnus Magnusson said about the geological history of Scotland is also true for Britain as a whole. There is indeed a fascinating story to tell, although some of the chapters are still far from complete. For the full story to unfold it is vital that the important rocks and landforms of Britain must be protected so that they can provide the necessary scientific resource for future work. And this may well utilise new scientific techniques yet to be discovered.

Britain was the cradle of modern geology, and observations made by British geologists in the eighteenth and nineteenth centuries laid the foundations of the science as we know it today. Many of the sites at which these observations were made continue to be conserved as a part of our national Earth heritage. The contribution that the geology of Britain has made to international science is as important today as it has ever been. British sites are world-renowned for providing the milestones that mark geological time and the benchmarks that define geological principles. There is every reason for us to take a special pride in this unrivalled Earth heritage.

Foreword

Since the heady, pioneering days in the early development of the Earth sciences, the study of the geology of Britain has continued to provide evidence to construct, and then test, theories about the development of the Earth and the processes that take place within its interior and on its surface. Geology today is as much about the future as it is about the past. By learning about past climates we can understand our present climate system better and thus how to evaluate the impact of future climatic changes.

The geology of Britain has contributed to our national wealth and so influenced our archaeological and industrial inheritance, from the Phoenicians trading for Cornish tin, to the coal and iron which created the Industrial Revolution and, now, to the oil and gas below our coastal seas which is essential to our economic well-being. The geologists of tomorrow, who will discover new economic resources and locate sites for new engineering works all over the world, are being trained in an environment of extraordinary geological quality.

Natural landforms create the environments within which the diverse flora and fauna of Britain live. Rocks provide the soil and influence the drainage conditions of biological habitats. Biological and geological forms and functions are inextricably linked to create a series of natural systems of immense richness and diversity.

Active conservation measures are required to protect the geology and landforms of Britain as an important and irreplaceable scientific, educational, cultural, aesthetic and potentially economic resource. If irreparable damage or loss was to occur then it is our own society that would be impoverished.

Conservation of geological and geomorphological sites has always been part of the responsibilities of the statutory nature conservation agencies. A major initiative to identify and describe the most important geological sites in Britain began in 1977, with the launching of the Geological Conservation Review. This book provides a description of the methods and practice of the Review, as well as a background account of the geological history of Britain which demonstrates clearly why the Earth heritage of this country is so important.

I am confident that this book will be an invaluable reference for those who wish to understand the Geological Conservation Review and for those who need to manage our extraordinarily diverse Earth heritage.

The Earl of Selborne KBE FRS
Chairman, Joint Nature Conservation Committee

An artist's impression of the Earth from space, as it might have appeared some 360 million years ago. The outline of present-day Britain is shown as a dotted line. Reproduced from F. W. Dunning et al. (1978) by permission of the Natural History Museum, London.

Chapter 1

The subject and purpose
of this volume

The purpose of this book is to explain why Britain's Earth heritage is important and how the national series of Earth heritage sites was identified in the Geological Conservation Review. It also describes how these sites are protected by law and how they are conserved.

This volume is intended primarily for all those with an interest in managing the land: owners and occupiers, managers, planners and those involved in the waste disposal, mineral extraction, construction and coastal engineering industries. It will also be of interest to professional and amateur Earth scientists, conservationists, and teachers, lecturers and students of the Earth sciences.

The geological history of Britain is fascinating. Since the cooling of the outer part of the Earth and the formation of the oceans, whole continents have moved around the planet, repeatedly coalescing into great land masses and fragmenting again. When continents collided, great mountain ranges, including the Alps and Himalayas of today, were formed and then eroded away. The rocks of Britain record a diversity of environmental conditions that unfolded over thousands of millions of years. For some of the time 'Britain' was located in the tropics. As it drifted northwards, great sandy deserts were replaced by equatorial forests and swamps only, in due course, to become desert once more. Shallow seas between land masses became isolated from their neighbouring oceans and dwindled away. Quiet landscapes were disrupted by erupting volcanoes, lava fields cooled, vents solidified and the volcanoes passed into history. In more recent ages, 'Britain' drifted into temperate latitudes. Glaciers and ice caps have repeatedly advanced and retreated over its surface, moulding and shaping the landscape. Even today, the appearance of the land continues to change; sand dunes shift, coastlines and river valleys evolve, rock weathers and landslips alter the shape of the countryside.

Just as the land and seas have changed over the ages, so have the life-forms they supported. Life evolved in the oceans in the form of unicellular marine organisms which helped to change the composition of the atmosphere. They eventually evolved into many types of multi-cellular organisms such as coral, predatory sea-

Figure 1. *Haytor Rocks, Dartmoor, is not only an important part of Britain's natural heritage for its aesthetic quality, but also for the Earth sciences. Study of the granite rock here has revealed important information about the cooling and crystallisation of molten rock. The rocks form an impressive 'tor', formed by weathering. Photo: S. Campbell.*

scorpions, ichthyosaurs and countless other invertebrates and vertebrates. Plants, and then animals, colonised the land. Forests came and went; giant horsetails, tree ferns, redwoods and magnolias successively dominated the landscape of their time. After the land plants came insects, amphibians, dinosaurs and other reptiles, birds, mammals and, eventually, human beings.

For over two hundred years, natural historians and scientists have been piecing together the evidence for the geological history of Britain. Careful observation and interpretation of the rocks in natural and man-made exposures, and the features of the landscape, have provided both the inspiration and the information needed to establish this history. But the picture is still far from complete, there are areas of uncertainty and controversy, and much remains to be done.

The legacy of the geological past — rocks, soils and landforms — comprises the **Earth heritage** of Britain (Figure 1). Much of this heritage is hidden beneath the land surface, but coastal cliffs, river gorges, cliffs, mountain crags, quarries, and road and railway cuttings provide opportunities for study. Just as some activities such as quarrying and road building have created many rock exposures, they can also destroy or obscure them. Coastal cliffs have been protected to prevent erosion, disused quarries and railway cuttings have been used as tipping sites, fossil-bearing rocks have been dug up and sold for profit, and sand and gravel have been extracted for aggregate. Much of this activity has to take place in a country where land has to serve many purposes. If they are uncontrolled, these activities may ultimately lead to the loss of the most important elements of our Earth heritage. It is necessary to identify the key sites and to safeguard their future.

The identification of the most important Earth heritage sites in Britain began 50 years ago. In 1977, the Nature Conservancy Council began a systematic review of the key Earth science localities. This was designed to identify, and help conserve, those sites of national and international importance in Britain. This review, known as the Geological Conservation Review, was completed in 1990, and is an international first. No other country has attempted such a systematic and comprehensive review of its Earth heritage.

The results of the Geological Conservation Review are being published in 42 volumes written for a specialist scientific readership. This introduction to the series is written for a wider audience and includes a glossary and list of suggestions for further reading.

Chapter 2

The need for
Earth heritage conservation

Many people are aware of the need for the conservation of the natural world. Reports about pollution, disappearing rain forests and the extinction of species have increased our perception of the need to protect the natural environment. Rocks, minerals, fossils, soils and landforms are an integral part of our natural world. The distribution of habitats, plants and animals depends not only upon climate, but also upon the geology and landscape.

As well as being a fundamental part of the natural world, geology and landscape have had a profound influence on society and civilisation. Our use of the land, for agriculture, forestry, mining, quarrying and for building homes and cities is intimately related to the underlying rocks, soils and landforms. Moreover, economic resources such as coal, oil, gas and metal ores have played an important role in the industrial development of Britain, particularly during the Industrial Revolution.

The heritage value of sites and the importance of conserving them can be summarised under six themes:

- ❏ the international significance of Earth heritage sites
- ❏ exceptional Earth heritage sites
- ❏ Earth science research
- ❏ environmental forecasting
- ❏ Earth heritage sites in education and training
- ❏ Earth heritage as a cultural and ecological resource.

THE INTERNATIONAL SIGNIFICANCE OF EARTH HERITAGE SITES

Much of the early knowledge of the history of the Earth was developed in Britain (*see* Chapter 3), and many British sites have played a part in the development of now universally applied principles of geology. These sites have great historical importance. For example, many of the names of periods of geological time are derived from Britain. Many other sites serve as international reference sections. By reference to these international 'standards' (Figure 2), the relative ages of rocks all over the world can be compared. Other internationally important British reference sites include those where rocks, minerals and fossils were first described. Such sites must be conserved so that they can continue to be used as the standard references.

Figure 2. *Dob's Linn, south-west Scotland. This internationally important site is officially recognised by the International Union of Geological Sciences (IUGS) as the reference section for the boundary between the Ordovician and Silurian Periods (see Figure 13). This boundary is used as the global standard for comparative purposes. For example, fossils and other rock attributes that occur at Dob's Linn can be compared with those in rocks elsewhere. Photo: C. C. J. MacFadyen.*

EXCEPTIONAL EARTH HERITAGE SITES

There are many sites in Britain which are of international importance because of their exceptional nature. For example, rocks from Charnwood in Leicestershire (Figure 3) have yielded some of the oldest multi-celled animal fossils in the world. Similarly, a site at Rhynie in Scotland (*see* Figure 46) contains some of the oldest known fossils of higher plants, insects, arachnids (mites and spiders) and crustaceans. They occur in an exceptionally well-preserved state; so much so, that the microscopic detail and

Figure 3. *The rocks of the Memorial Crags at Bradgate Park, Charnwood Forest, Leicestershire and reconstruction of* Charnia masoni, *a primitive life-form. The rocks exposed in the crags are probably 650–700 million years old.*

Occasionally, the rock surfaces show impressions of some of the first forms of life — imprints of soft bodies of some of the earliest large multi-celled organisms. These include the remains of jelly-fish and sea-pen-like animals, including Charnia masoni.

The preservation of soft-bodied animals is rare because they usually decay very soon after death or are eaten by scavengers. In this case, the animals were probably engulfed by a catastrophic event, perhaps the mass slumping of sediment, which trapped the fauna. The animals became preserved in the sediment, which eventually became rock. Because of the worldwide rarity of the preservation of these early life-forms, Bradgate Park is of great importance to the study of early life. Photo © Leicestershire Museums.

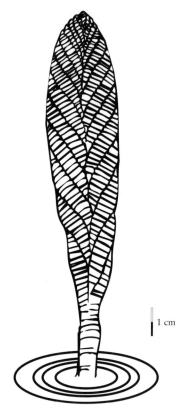

1 cm

cell structures of the original organisms can be studied. Such sites are rare and are an irreplaceable part of the Earth heritage of the world.

EARTH SCIENCE RESEARCH

The geology of Britain provides a resource for research (Figure 4). Natural rock outcrops and landforms, and artificial exposures of rock created in the course of mining, quarrying and engineering works, are crucial to our understanding of Britain's Earth heritage. Future research may help to resolve current geological problems, support new theories and develop innovative techniques or ideas only if sites are available for future study.

ENVIRONMENTAL FORECASTING

Understanding how processes have operated in the past — the climate system, soil formation, desertification and the evolution and extinction of plants and animals — contributes to our comprehension of the problems of the present. We may be able to use this knowledge to forecast volcanic activity, earthquakes or changes in climate. For example, by studying the dynamics of natural systems, such as rivers and coasts, it may be possible to predict how land and coastal processes will operate in the future. This will aid flood prediction and management, the mapping of physically hazardous areas and coastal management.

Evidence from the sediments and landforms,

Figure 4. *Moel Tryfan, Gwynedd. This is a historically important site, 400 metres above sea level, that consists of sand and gravel containing fossils of sea-shells. It was cited as evidence for the biblical flood by the Diluvialists. Subsequently it was interpreted as a glacial deposit carried from the sea bed by an Irish Sea ice sheet during the last ice age, about 23,000 years ago. This has a bearing on the dimensions of the last Irish Sea ice sheet, the extent to which it may have depressed the Earth's crust, and the degree of crustal 'rebound' after glaciation (see also Figure 10). It is a subject of ongoing research. Photo: S. Campbell.*

Figure 5. *Traeth Mawr, Brecon Beacons. This site has a sequence of peat and clay deposits which contain a pollen record reflecting marked fluctuations in climate from 14,000 years ago to the present. It provides information about the nature and rate of climatic and environmental changes. The photograph shows a general view of the site. Photo: S. Campbell.*

EARTH HERITAGE SITES IN EDUCATION AND TRAINING

particularly over the past 15,000 years, shows that the natural environment is highly sensitive to climatic change. Further study will throw light on possible future changes in the climate system and the faunal, floral and environmental responses to such changes (Figure 5).

As well as recording natural changes, the sediments in lakes and bogs provide records of the effects of human activities on the environment through pollution, vegetation changes (including forest clearance) and soil erosion. These records are important for assessing the effects of current human activity.

Earth heritage sites are essential for training and education. Students and teachers need sites for practical demonstration of the principles of geology and to illustrate the processes of landscape evolution (Figure 6a).

The use of rocks and minerals, water and the energy derived from fossil and nuclear fuels, are at the centre of modern society and are essential to its economic well-being. Trained geologists are needed to locate and extract oil and gas (Figure 6b), metal ores and the raw materials for the construction industry, such as clays for brick-making, stone for building and aggregates for concrete. Geologists also discover aquifers, and locate reservoirs and sites for major engineering projects.

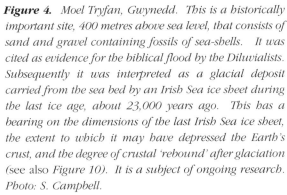

Figure 6. *Kimmeridge Bay, Dorset.* *(a)* *The site is an important location for training courses, universities, schools and geological societies. The photograph shows members of the Dorset Geologists' Association Group visiting the site which displays organic-rich rocks similar to those that have generated oil and gas under the North Sea. Photo: R. Hannock, Dorset Geologists' Association Group.*

(b) *Oil was discovered at Kimmeridge in 1956. Since then, the wellsite has continued to produce 100 barrels of oil a day. Photograph copyright Sillson Photography/BP Exploration Ltd. Reproduced with kind permission.*

Figure 7. *Geology is an inseparable part of the natural world. The photograph shows an area of limestone pavement at Scar Close National Nature Reserve in North Yorkshire. Water has percolated through joints in the exposed limestone and produced deep clefts (grykes). In the sheltered grykes, unusual plant life, including many rare ferns and orchids, has developed. The micro-climate in the grykes is more like that of woodland than exposed hillside. Photo: P. Wakely.*

THE EARTH HERITAGE AS A CULTURAL AND ECOLOGICAL RESOURCE

Geological features contribute to the aesthetic and ecological quality of landscape as part of the cultural heritage of Britain (Figure 7). Geology trails, visitor centres, museums, show caves and mines open to the public, enhance and deepen our appreciation of the Earth heritage. Some places attract hundreds of thousands of visitors each year.

Chapter 3

An introduction to the geological history of Britain

THE IMPORTANCE OF SITES

In the previous chapter, a variety of sites were introduced to illustrate the need for Earth heritage conservation. Evidence from many sites, where rocks and landforms were formed at different times and places, has allowed a historical sequence of geological events and previous geographies to be built up. These rocks and landforms at Earth heritage sites are still important for revealing new evidence, and for refining theories concerning their method and date of formation. To illustrate the importance of sites to the Earth sciences, three are described which show how information about Earth history can be inferred from the evidence they contain.

Salisbury Crags and Arthur's Seat, Edinburgh

Research began at this site over two centuries ago and the Crags played a most significant role in the early establishment of geological science. In *Theory of the Earth* (1795) James Hutton advocated the Vulcanist theory that the crystalline rocks of Salisbury Crags were formed by the intrusion

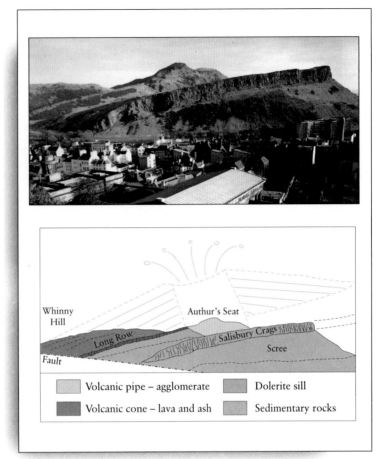

Figure 8. *Salisbury Crags and Arthur's Seat, Edinburgh. The diagram shows the relationship between the geology and the ancient volcano. Photograph reproduced by permission of the Director, British Geological Survey. NERC copyright reserved. Diagram after Wilson (1994).*

and cooling of hot molten rock (magma) and not, as was the contemporary Neptunist view, as a precipitate from a primordial sea. Study and interpretation of the site was therefore vital in deciding the controversy between Vulcanists and Neptunists.

The igneous rock is sandwiched within sedimentary rocks which were baked as the molten rock intruded (Figure 8). Much of the overlying sedimentary rock has been removed by erosion and quarrying. An igneous rock mass, such as that at Salisbury Crags, which lies parallel to the beds is called a sill (*see* Figure 12).

The principle that processes observed today can be used to interpret those which occurred in the past is an important tool in Earth science. By making comparisons with contemporary active volcanoes and volcanic rocks, it is possible to find evidence in the Edinburgh area of former lava lakes, volcanic vents (now preserved as lava blocks in volcanic ash), numerous lava flows, volcanic ash layers and a sequence of lake sediments which accumulated within and adjacent to the volcanic vents. Arthur's Seat consists of two pipes of an ancient volcano which were active 350 million years ago. The site also shows the effects of earth movement, which has caused the eastward tilt of the rocks. The relationship between the original volcano and Arthur's Seat is shown in Figure 8.

The site is now one of the most heavily used educational areas in Britain, and is of international significance as one of the most intensively investigated ancient volcanoes in the world.

Figure 9. *Cliffs near Barton-on-Sea, Hampshire. The cliffs are made up of sediments deposited in marine, brackish and freshwater environments. Where these sediments occur inland, there are no natural outcrops, the land largely being built over or farmed, and there are few opportunities to see vertical sections through the strata. On the coast, however, fresh sections occur as the sea erodes the cliffs, but they can be obscured by coastal defence works and landslides. Photo: C. D. Prosser.*

Barton Cliffs, Hampshire

These cliffs (Figure 9) are internationally known for the rich and diverse fossil assemblage that they have yielded. These fossils and the sediments in which they are contained provide evidence for their contemporary environments. Comparisons with present-day environments assist this process further.

The abundant fossils at Barton Cliffs — molluscs, reptiles, mammals, birds and plants — have also enabled correlations to be made with rocks of similar age in other parts of the world. Thus the exposures at Barton are an international reference section or 'stratotype', and sediments all over the world of an equivalent age are called Bartonian, which corresponds to a span of time between 41 and 35 million years ago.

Islay and Jura, the Inner Hebrides

Raised cliff-lines, shore-platforms and shingle beach ridges, up to 30 metres above present sea level, occur along the coastlines of Islay and Jura in the Inner Hebrides (Figure 10). They provide evidence about changes in the relative levels of land and sea during the late-glacial period, at the end of the last ice age.

During an ice age, large volumes of ocean water become locked up in ice sheets and glaciers and, in consequence, the global sea level falls. In those areas actually covered by ice, such as Scotland, the weight of ice depresses the Earth's crust below the position of the modern sea level. At the end of an ice age, water is returned to the oceans by melting ice sheets and the global sea

level rises. In the glaciated areas, the Earth's crust recovers, or rebounds, as the weight of the ice is removed. It is a complex process because three factors are involved: the *ice* itself is in retreat and allows the rising *sea level* to flood the depressed crust, and *the Earth's crust* is also recovering. These processes occurred at variable rates. But when the rate of sea-level rise and the rate of crustal recovery were approximately the same, major shoreline features were fashioned. This happened at ocean levels below that of modern sea level. After the ice age, when the Earth's major ice sheets had melted, when sea level had been restored to its modern position and the Earth's crust had recovered to its pre-glacial position, the late-glacial shorelines were uplifted above modern sea level.

The late-glacial coastal features of Islay and Jura were formed when global sea level was below the present, and when the Earth's crust was locally depressed by the weight of the Scottish ice sheet. Both the global sea level and the Earth's crust of the Inner Hebrides have now recovered to their pre-glacial position. The coastal features that were formed between approximately 15,000 and 12,000 years ago, below the modern sea level, have been uplifted and now lie up to 30 metres above sea level.

THE GEOLOGY OF BRITAIN

Introduction

Geological maps provide the framework in time and space which permits stories from individual sites to be synthesised to

Figure 10. *The coasts of the islands of Islay and Jura in the Inner Hebrides display raised ice-age shorelines, especially spectacular shingle beach ridges. At one locality, up to 31 unvegetated shingle ridges occur up to 30 metres above present sea level. These were formed at the end of the last ice age, when sea level and the level of the Earth's crust in the Inner Hebrides were below modern sea level. These late-glacial shorelines and shingle ridges were uplifted to their present position when the Earth's crust recovered from the load of the ice sheet. Photo: J. E. Gordon.*

produce the geological history of Britain. Figure 11 is a simplified map showing the distribution of rocks across the British Isles. It does not show sands, gravels and other sediments deposited recently by rivers, or those left behind during the ice ages. Exploring this map and its key provides an insight into the immensity of geological time, and the origins of the great variety of rocks found over such a relatively small area of the planet.

The origin of rocks

The key to Figure 11 is divided into three sections, reflecting the division of rocks into three major groups according to the way in which they were formed: sedimentary, igneous and metamorphic.

Sedimentary rocks

Weathering and erosion of pre-existing rocks at the Earth's surface yields a vast amount of rock debris that is

subsequently transported by rivers and marine currents to produce sediments such as sands and muds. After burial beneath further layers of sediment, these deposits become consolidated to produce sedimentary rocks such as sandstones, mudstones and shales. In addition to being formed from fragments of pre-existing rock, sedimentary rocks such as limestones are produced by accumulation of the calcareous skeletons of organisms, for example corals or bivalve shells (like those commonly seen on British beaches). For example, the accumulation of the microscopic calcareous skeletal elements of plankton produces a very fine-grained limestone known as chalk.

Igneous rocks

Rocks that have crystallised from molten material (magma) consist of individual interlocking angular mineral grains, unlike sedimentary rocks, in which the mineral grains or rock fragments show some degree of rounding.

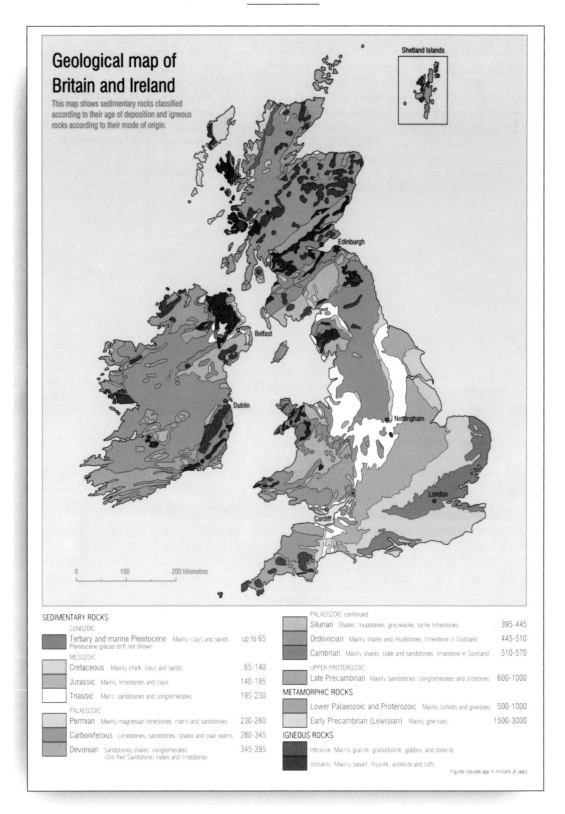

Geological map of Britain and Ireland

This map shows sedimentary rocks classified according to their age of deposition and igneous rocks according to their mode of origin.

Shetland Islands

Edinburgh

Belfast

Dublin

Nottingham

London

Cardiff

0   100   200 kilometres

SEDIMENTARY ROCKS

CENOZOIC

Tertiary and marine Pleistocene   Mainly clays and sands   up to 65
Pleistocene glacial drift not shown

MESOZOIC

Cretaceous   Mainly chalk, clays and sands   65-140

Jurassic   Mainly limestones and clays   140-195

Triassic   Marls, sandstones and conglomerates   195-230

PALAEOZOIC

Permian   Mainly magnesian limestones, marls and sandstones   230-280

Carboniferous   Limestones, sandstones, shales and coal seams   280-345

Devonian   Sandstones, shales, conglomerates   345-395
(Old Red Sandstone) slates and limestones

PALAEOZOIC continued

Silurian   Shales, mudstones, greywacke; some limestones   395-445

Ordovician   Mainly shales and mudstones; limestone in Scotland   445-510

Cambrian   Mainly shales, slate and sandstones; limestone in Scotland   510-570

UPPER PROTEROZOIC

Late Precambrian   Mainly sandstones, conglomerates and siltstones   600-1000

METAMORPHIC ROCKS

Lower Palaeozoic and Proterozoic   Mainly schists and gneisses   500-1000

Early Precambrian (Lewisian)   Mainly gneisses   1500-3000

IGNEOUS ROCKS

Intrusive   Mainly granite, granodiorite, gabbro, and dolerite

Volcanic   Mainly basalt, rhyolite, andesite and tuffs

Figures indicate age in millions of years

Figure 11.   *Geological map of Britain and Ireland. Each period, although represented on the map by a single colour, may include a variety of rock types. For example, the Silurian (pale mauve) includes shales and mudstones, and the Jurassic (olive-green) includes limestones and clays. This simplification is necessary to be able to show the geology of Britain on such a small map. See glossary for definition of terms. Reproduced by permission of the Director, British Geological Survey. NERC copyright reserved.*

Igneous rocks may have cooled at the Earth's surface, in which case they are called *extrusive* (or volcanic, as in the key to Figure 11), or beneath the Earth's surface as *intrusive* rocks (Figure 12). Granite, granodiorite, gabbros and dolerite referred to in the key to Figure 11 are all examples of intrusive rocks, whereas basalt, andesite and rhyolite are extrusive.

Metamorphic rocks

Rocks which have been altered from their original state by heat and/or pressure are known as metamorphic rocks. Such alteration occurs from several to tens of kilometres beneath the Earth's surface. Slates are grained metamorphic rocks formed from mudstones, and are included under sedimentary rocks in the key to Figure 11. Schists and gneisses are coarser crystalline metamorphic rocks which formed deep within mountain belts.

Geological time

The key to the geological map shown in Figure 11 subdivides sedimentary rocks into *Cenozoic, Mesozoic, Palaeozoic* and *Upper Proterozoic*. These terms correspond to particular spans of time (the numbers to the right of the key to Figure 11 are ages in millions of years). The first three are called eras of geological time and together constitute the Phanerozoic Eon, which is characterised by rocks containing fossils of animals with mineralised skeletons. The term 'Phanerozoic' was originally coined from the Greek words for 'evident' and 'life'. The time before the Phanerozoic Eon is divided into two other eons, the *Proterozoic* and the *Archaean*, which together are often called the *Precambrian*. The term 'Upper Proterozoic' on the map refers to the most recent part of the Proterozoic Eon. The eras of the Phanerozoic are themselves divided into *periods* whose names are given in bold type next to the colour key (e.g. Permian, Cambrian). So for the sedimentary rocks, each colour represents rocks formed during a particular period.

Eons, eras and periods are shown systematically in Figure 13 as time divisions of the *stratigraphic column*. The column is arranged in chronological order with the oldest period at the bottom and the youngest at the top, just as sedimentary rocks of these ages would be stacked now if they had been left undisturbed since they were laid down.

As stated in Chapter 1, Britain was the cradle of

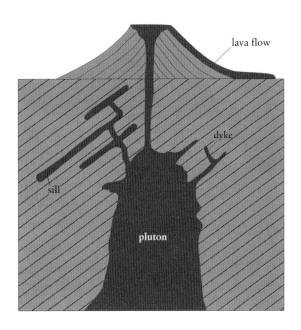

Figure 12. *The principal occurrence of igneous rocks. Extrusive: lava flows; Intrusive: sills, dykes and plutons. Molten rock erupting from volcanoes may also produce ash (referred to as tuff in the key to Figure 11). After Wilson (1994).*

the science of geology, resulting in many of the divisions of geological time shown in Figure 13 being named here by pioneering geologists, as shown in Table 1. These geologists realised that sediments deposited during a particular period of geological time are characterised by distinctive assemblages of fossils (*see* information box on page 19) which enable rock successions of the same relative age to be identified in many parts of the world. It may seem surprising that geologists do not use dates in the same way as historians. There are two main reasons. First, the periods within each of the eras were recognised by early geologists before there was any agreement about the age of the Earth, or the duration of the periods. The advent of methods of dating rocks using the small amounts of radioactive elements present in them enabled the relative scale represented by the periods to be calibrated in millions of years. But even today, this subdivision is not precise because of experimental errors and the different versions of such calibrations in use. This is the second reason that the names of the geological periods are used rather than dates — because it is less confusing than using numbers.

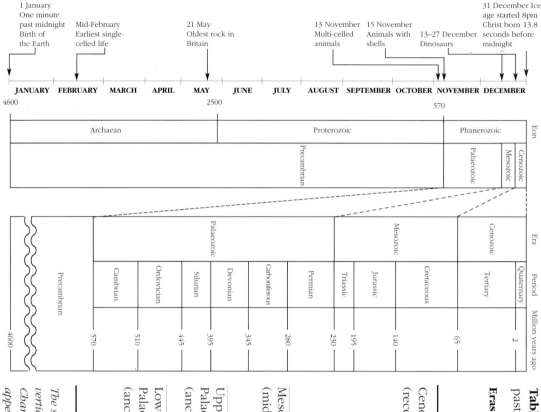

Figure 13. The stratigraphic column. At the top, key events in Earth history are compressed into one year to illustrate the immensity of the geological timescale. After Grayson (1993).

Timeline labels:
- 1 January One minute past midnight Birth of the Earth
- Mid-February Earliest single-celled life
- 21 May Oldest rock in Britain
- 13 November Multi-celled animals
- 15 November Animals with shells
- 13–27 December Dinosaurs
- 31 December Ice age started 8pm Christ born 13.8 seconds before midnight

JANUARY FEBRUARY MARCH APRIL MAY JUNE JULY AUGUST SEPTEMBER OCTOBER NOVEMBER DECEMBER
4600   2500   570

Eon: Archaean | Proterozoic | Phanerozoic
(Precambrian — Palaeozoic — Mesozoic — Cenozoic)

Era: Cenozoic, Mesozoic, Palaeozoic, Precambrian
Period: Quaternary, Tertiary, Cretaceous, Jurassic, Triassic, Permian, Carboniferous, Devonian, Silurian, Ordovician, Cambrian, Precambrian
Million years ago: 2, 65, 140, 195, 230, 280, 345, 395, 445, 510, 570, 4600

Table 1. Origin of the names of the time periods in the stratigraphic column for the past 570 million years.

Eras	Periods in bold type, epochs in normal type		Age of base in millions of years	Country where defined	Derivation of name
Cenozoic (recent life)	**Quaternary**	Holocene	0.01	England	Holos: whole
		Pleistocene	1.6	England	Pleiston: most
	Tertiary	Pliocene	5.3	England	Pleios: more
		Miocene	23	England	Meion: less
		Oligocene	36.5	Germany	Oligos: few
		Eocene	53	England	Eos: dawn
		Palaeocene	65	England	Palaeos: old
Mesozoic (middle life)	**Cretaceous**		140	France	Creta: chalk
	Jurassic		195	Switzerland	Jura Mountains
	Triassic		230	Germany	Three-fold division recognised in Germany
Upper Palaeozoic (ancient life)	**Permian**		280	Russia	The town of Perm in Russia
	Carboniferous		345	England	Carbon: coal
	Devonian		395	England	Devon
Lower Palaeozoic (ancient life)	**Silurian**		445	Wales	Silures: Celts of the Welsh Borders
	Ordovician		510	Wales	Ordovices: Celts of North Wales
	Cambrian		570	Wales	Cambria: Latin for Wales

The stratigraphic column is the array of geological time units that results from stacking them vertically, with the oldest at the base, overlain by successively younger units. In the 1830s, Sir Charles Lyell recognised that in the Cenozoic (sometimes spelt Cainozoic) Era modern species appear as fossils, becoming progressively more abundant in younger sediments. For example, 3% of Eocene species are alive today, and as many as 30–50% of Pliocene species exist today. Lyell chose to use Greek prefixes to subdivide the Era according to this observation. After Wilson (1994).

Fossils

Palaeontology is the study of fossils. Fossils are the remains or 'traces' of plants or animals which have been buried by natural processes and then permanently preserved. These include skeletal materials (e.g. bones and shells), tracks, trails and borings made by living organisms, as well as their excrement. They also include the impressions (moulds or casts) of organisms on rock surfaces, and even actual biological material. For fossilisation to occur, the death of a plant or animal must normally be followed by its rapid burial, otherwise the remains will be physically broken up or destroyed by scavengers or by chemical and biological decay.

The photograph shows a fossil ammonite, Asteroceras obtusum, *from Charmouth, Dorset. Although superficially like a snail shell, it is actually the remains of a cephalopod. Modern relatives include the squid, octopus and* Nautilus. *Because of the relative abundance of ammonite fossils, and the relatively rapid evolution of different species, they provide useful 'markers' for comparing ages of rocks at different places. Photo: K. N. Page.*

Once the organic trace has been buried it may be preserved as unaltered material, such as original skeletal material, mammoths frozen in permafrost or insects in amber. Alternatively it may be petrified. In this case, minerals have either replaced the previous cells or tissue, or filled in pores in the original material. Sometimes the sediment around a fossil may survive but the fossil itself is dissolved away, leaving a mould which may later become infilled with another mineral. This creates a cast of the original fossil.

Fossils are named in the same way as living plants and animals, and are important as a means of determining the relative ages of rocks. They can be used to reconstruct a detailed history of life on Earth and explain the rate and pattern of evolution and the nature of ancient environments and ecosystems. The importance of fossils is illustrated in the diagram.

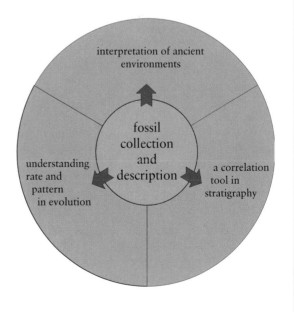

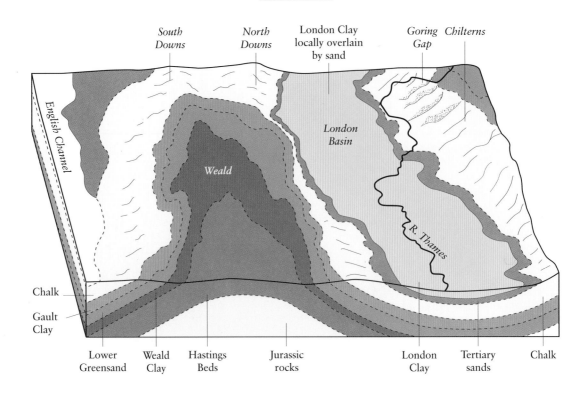

Figure 14. *The geological structure of south-east England, showing major topographic features associated with the Wealden Anticline, and the London Basin (syncline). Note that the Hastings Beds, Weald Clay, Lower Greensand, Gault Clay and Chalk comprise the Cretaceous shown on Figure 13. After Edmunds (1983).*

Some geological patterns

Even a fairly superficial examination of the geological map of Britain shown in Figure 11 reveals some significant patterns in the distribution of ages and types of rock that offer clues about the geological history of the area. South-east of a line between the mouths of the Rivers Tees and Exe there are broad bands of Permian, Triassic, Jurassic, Cretaceous and Tertiary rocks. This pattern is relatively simple compared with that displayed by older rocks to the north-west. The Permian–Tertiary rocks reflect the simple geological structure underlying this area. For example, north of London, the rock layers are inclined gently (by a matter of a few degrees) to the east and south-east, and so are younger in these directions. London is situated in the centre of a 'basin' in which rocks of Tertiary age are preserved. This is because a broad *fold*, termed a *syncline* exists here. To the south of the London Basin another fold occurs, bending the strata upwards into an arch, or *anticline*, so that older strata are exposed in the Weald (Figure 14). The North and South Downs are the topographic expression of the

Figure 15. *The areas of higher ground in Britain. Nearly all of these are coincident with the relics of past mountain chains (compare with Figure 16). After Wilson (1994).*

Some geological patterns

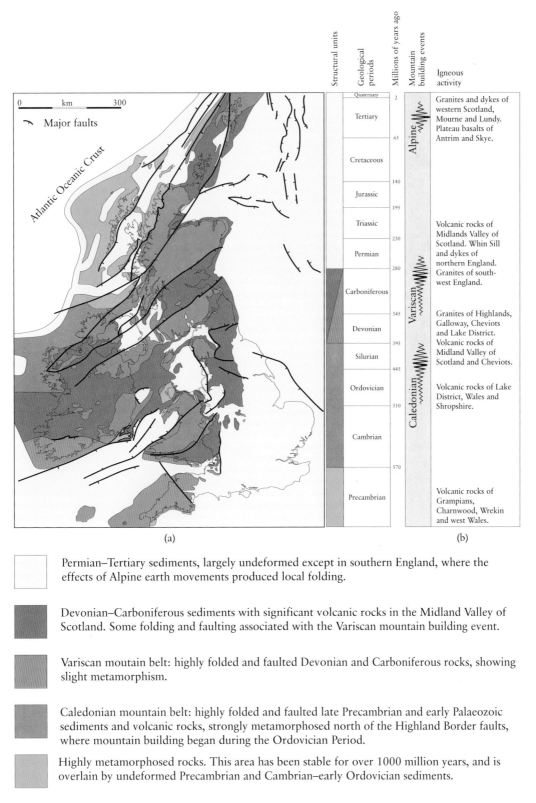

Structural units | Geological periods | Millions of years ago | Mountain building events | Igneous activity

Geological periods	Millions of years ago	Mountain building events	Igneous activity
Quaternary	2	Alpine	Granites and dykes of western Scotland, Mourne and Lundy. Plateau basalts of Antrim and Skye.
Tertiary	65		
Cretaceous	140		
Jurassic	195		
Triassic	230	Variscan	Volcanic rocks of Midlands Valley of Scotland. Whin Sill and dykes of northern England. Granites of south-west England.
Permian	280		
Carboniferous	345		
Devonian	395		Granites of Highlands, Galloway, Cheviots and Lake District. Volcanic rocks of Midland Valley of Scotland and Cheviots.
Silurian	445	Caledonian	
Ordovician	510		Volcanic rocks of Lake District, Wales and Shropshire.
Cambrian	570		
Precambrian			Volcanic rocks of Grampians, Charnwood, Wrekin and west Wales.

(a)   (b)

Permian–Tertiary sediments, largely undeformed except in southern England, where the effects of Alpine earth movements produced local folding.

Devonian–Carboniferous sediments with significant volcanic rocks in the Midland Valley of Scotland. Some folding and faulting associated with the Variscan mountain building event.

Variscan moutain belt: highly folded and faulted Devonian and Carboniferous rocks, showing slight metamorphism.

Caledonian mountain belt: highly folded and faulted late Precambrian and early Palaeozoic sediments and volcanic rocks, strongly metamorphosed north of the Highland Border faults, where mountain building began during the Ordovician Period.

Highly metamorphosed rocks. This area has been stable for over 1000 million years, and is overlain by undeformed Precambrian and Cambrian–early Ordovician sediments.

Figure 16. *British mountain belts.* **(a)** *Map showing the distribution of the major ancient mountain belts of Britain. Faults are major planar structures across which rocks have been displaced vertically or laterally. For example, the area in Scotland between the Highland Boundary Fault and the Southern Uplands Faults has been displaced downwards between the two faults, whereas lateral displacement occurred along the Great Glen Fault.* **(b)** *Chart summarising the ages of mountain building events and igneous activity. After Dunning* et al. *(1978).*

Mountain building episodes

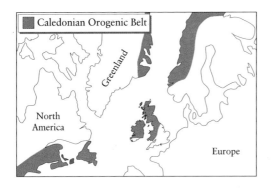

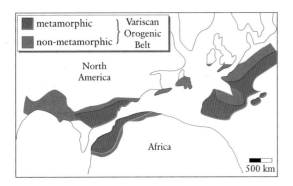

Figure 17. *The distribution of the Caledonian and Variscan mountain belts on a map of the continents reassembled to the positions they occupied before the opening of the present-day Atlantic Ocean. Early protagonists of continental drift used reconstructions such as these as evidence in favour of the former unity of now widely separated continents. After Wilson (1994).*

Figure 16 shows the distribution of rocks in Britain associated with mountain building episodes. The Caledonian mountain belt resulted from the closure of a proto-Atlantic ocean between 'North America' and 'Greenland' and 'Europe'. The Variscan mountain belt was formed by closure of a former ocean which separated southern 'Britain' and most of 'Belgium' from the rest of 'Europe'. By closing the present-day Atlantic Ocean (Figure 17), the distribution of rocks caught up in these two mountain building episodes shows that they were once relatively long but narrow regions. The global pattern of crustal movements that causes mountain building (often referred to as 'orogenesis') is explained on the following pages.

Mountain building results in the deformation of previously deposited sediments and volcanic rocks to produce complex fold structures. This deformation also results in the thickening of the Earth's crust, so that some rocks are buried deep beneath the Earth's surface, where extremely high temperatures and pressures produce metamorphic rocks. The thickening of the crust results in uplift, as the rocks that comprise mountain belts are less dense than those beneath, and so they 'float' on deeper layers, much like an iceberg floats in water. As with icebergs, the deeper the submerged part, the higher the relief at the surface.

MOUNTAIN BUILDING AND PLATE TECTONICS

As already stated, mountain building is linked to the closing of former oceans. Today (and in the geological past) oceans are floored by crustal material that has a greater density than continental crust. As shown in Figure 18, the crust forms the thin outer skin of the Earth. Beneath it, in a concentrically layered structure, is the mantle and the core. So the Earth is rather like a spherical avocado pear. The thin green skin represents the crust, the yellow flesh the mantle, and the stone at the centre the core.

It is known from a variety of lines of evidence (including direct measurement from satellites) that horizontal movements occur in the Earth's crust. In fact, different parts of the crust move in different directions. The crust consists of a series of slabs or tectonic plates: where they collide or move apart, there are zones of earthquakes and volcanic activity, but there is little activity away

Wealden Anticline, produced respectively by northward and southward inclinations of the Chalk. The Chalk extends beneath the London Basin, reappearing to the north-west, where it forms the Chiltern Hills (here, it is inclined to the south-east).

The regions exhibiting more complex patterns visible in the western and northern areas of Figure 11 are generally highland areas (Figure 15). These are formed of Palaeozoic or older rocks, from sedimentary, igneous and metamorphic origins. These harder rocks are more resistant to erosion than the Mesozoic and Tertiary sedimentary rocks to the east and south-east. In fact, these areas are relics of former mountainous areas comparable in grandeur with the Alps or Himalayas of today.

Figure 18. *The structure of the Earth.*
(a) *Diagrammatic section through the Earth showing the core, mantle and crust. The crust is too thin to show to scale on this diagram: variations in its thickness are depicted in* *(b)*, *a generalised section through the Earth's crust showing variations in the thickness of continental and oceanic crust. Oceanic crust is between 2.8 and 2.9 times denser than water, and is similar in composition to rocks such as basalt and gabbro; continental crust is less dense (2.6 to 2.8 times as dense as water), with a composition similar to granite. Continental crust is less dense and much thicker than oceanic crust, so it floats higher on the mantle. After Wilson (1994).*

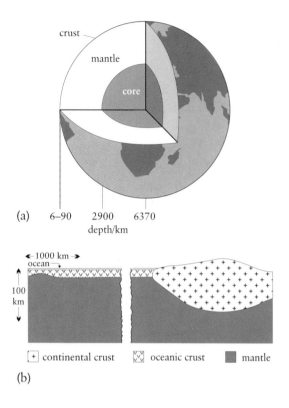

from the boundaries between the plates.

Figure 19 shows the plate boundaries associated with South America and Africa, two continents that are moving slowly apart at about four centimetres per year — twice the rate at which human fingernails grow. This means that the South Atlantic is getting wider. In fact, new oceanic crust is being formed along the Mid-Atlantic Ridge as basaltic magma wells up from the mantle to form both intrusive and extrusive igneous rocks. The ridge is associated with a narrow zone of shallow earthquakes.

To the west of South America, the Pacific oceanic crust is moving eastwards, plunging beneath the continental crust, where it enters a hotter region and begins to melt. The resultant magma rises upwards, melting some of the continental crust on its way to produce granites. Some of the magmas, which are very viscous, do reach the surface and cause explosive volcanic activity. This plate collision zone is also characterised by a zone of earthquakes beneath South America, as well as an ocean trench and the Andean mountain belt.

Figure 20 shows the distribution of the crustal plates around the world. Most of the plate boundaries shown on this map fall into three categories — constructive, destructive and conservative — and can be described as follows:

Figure 19. *The relationships of three crustal plates in the Earth's southern hemisphere. The thickness of the crustal layers is not to scale. New oceanic crust is constantly forming along the Mid-Atlantic Ridge. After Wyllie (1976).*

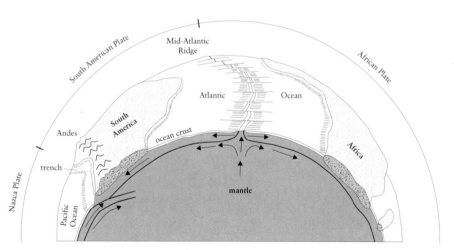

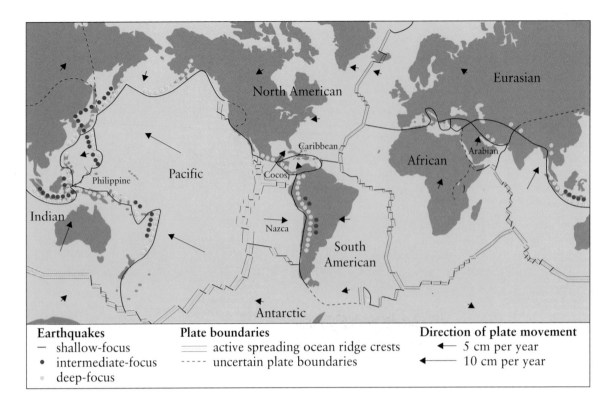

Figure 20. *The present distribution of crustal plates and the earthquake activity at their boundaries. All the constructive plate boundaries are regions of shallow earthquakes, whereas deeper-focus earthquake zones mark the location of destructive plate boundaries. The rates at which ocean crust is forming at constructive plate boundaries are shown schematically by the width between the parallel lines used to depict them. The directions of plate movement are shown by arrows, the lengths of which are proportional to the rate of movement: the shorter the arrow, the slower the plate is moving. After Gass et al. (1972).*

❑ *Constructive plate boundaries:* where basaltic magma rises from the mantle to form ocean ridges such as that running down the middle of the Atlantic. They are also characterised by shallow earthquakes (down to 5 km depth).

❑ *Destructive plate boundaries:* where oceanic crust plunges beneath continental crust. This process is called subduction: it is associated with deep ocean trenches and an inclined zone of earthquakes down to depths of several hundred kilometres. Subduction results in the melting of crustal material which rises to form plutons (*see* Figure 12) within the overlying continental crust, and if they reach the surface they cause explosive volcanic activity. Destructive plate boundaries also occur where two slabs of continental crust collide (such as in the Himalayan region today). Most of the Pacific Ocean is ringed by destructive plate margins; on its western side many such margins are marked by ocean trenches and associated volcanic islands arranged in an arc-like pattern, such as the Japanese islands.

❑ *Conservative plate boundaries:* where plates slide past each other, causing shallow earthquakes (the best known example is the San Andreas Fault in California).

What causes the movement of crustal plates? Basically, plate movement is the mechanism by which the Earth loses its internal heat generated by the breakdown of radioactive elements present in the crust and mantle. The internal heat drives a series of convection currents in the mantle which in turn drive plate movement (Figure 19), although the exact linkage between the currents and the plates is not clear. Are they pushed apart along constructive boundaries, or pulled down along destructive boundaries? As yet there is no consensus among Earth scientists.

Figure 21 shows, in cross-section, an idealised sequence of events in a cycle of ocean opening and 'closing', culminating in mountain building.

Figure 21. *Sequence of events in a cycle of ocean opening and closing, culminating in continental collision. It is possible for both plate margins to be subjected to subduction (as happened during the Caledonian mountain building in Britain), although this is not shown here.*

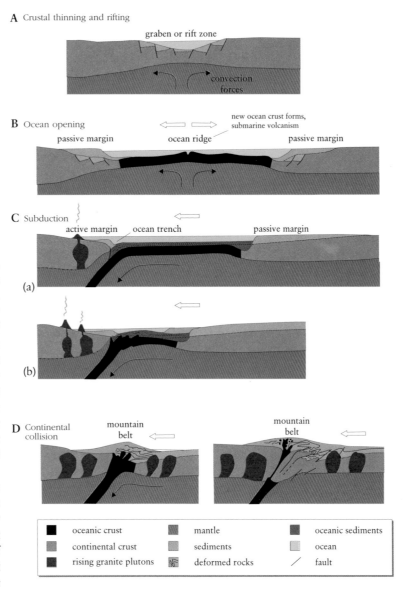

A Crustal thinning and rifting

B Ocean opening

C Subduction

(a)

(b)

D Continental collision

■ oceanic crust	▨ mantle	■ oceanic sediments
■ continental crust	▨ sediments	☐ ocean
■ rising granite plutons	▨ deformed rocks	⁄ fault

As the mountain belt is uplifted it is eroded, and sediments derived from it are deposited in neighbouring lowland areas, or in new oceans formed nearby if the continental crust splits up once more. As the mountains are eroded, they become partly covered by sedimentary rocks which overlie the older deformed rocks with an angular discordance, producing a major unconformity (*see* Figures 29 and 37).

Thus plate tectonics is the driving force behind mountain building. The formation of new oceans and their subsequent 'closure' produce a variety of rock types and structures that enable past plate tectonic processes to be interpreted from the rock record. At destructive plate margins, sedimentary rocks are folded, faulted and deeply buried, leading to metamorphism. Igneous processes along such margins result in the formation of huge masses of intrusive igneous rocks above which explosive volcanoes occur. Most of the granite shown on the geological map in Figure 11 was produced at destructive plate margins. All these processes result in thickening of the crust, which then rides higher on the underlying mantle to produce mountain belts. Such uplifted areas are affected by increased rates of erosion, and sediments accumulate on the margins of the newly deformed continental crust. The Devonian and Triassic sediments shown in Figure 11 were respectively derived largely from the uplifted Caledonian and Variscan mountains.

A GEOLOGICAL HISTORY OF BRITAIN

The Precambrian rocks of Britain

Over 85% of Earth history is represented by the Precambrian Era, the time between consolidation of the Earth's crust and the beginning of the Cambrian Period, about 570 million years ago. Less is known about these rocks than those formed during the last 570 million years of the geological history of Britain, because most of the early rocks have been eroded, deformed, metamorphosed or buried beneath younger rocks.

No trace has yet been found anywhere on Earth of rocks which date from the first 600 million years of the Earth's history, but rocks and minerals approximately 4000 million years old have now been found in most of the major continents. These rocks provide evidence of the nature of the early Earth.

During the Precambrian there was more rapid movement of the plates of the crust because of higher levels of heat production (caused by radioactive decay) and because the crust was still forming and was thinner. Consequently, many Precambrian rocks have undergone at least one episode of mountain building (orogeny), and some may have undergone several.

The oldest Precambrian rocks to be found in Britain are the Lewisian gneisses (Figure 22a, coloured pink in Figure 11), in the north-west Highlands and the Western Isles. They were formed over a period of 2,000 million years and the oldest were formed some 3,300 million years ago. These gneisses show evidence of several episodes of deformation and the intrusion of igneous rock, both associated with mountain building. These early crustal rocks were later overlain by Torridonian sediments, and the Moine and the Dalradian metamorphic rocks that show evidence of a long and complex geological history. These underlie large parts of northern Scotland (grey-green in Figure 11). Sedimentary and volcanic rocks of Precambrian age are also found in Anglesey (Figure 22b), the Welsh Borders, the Malverns and the Midlands.

Rocks which formed at the end of the Precambrian show evidence of animal life, and jellyfish-like fossils can be found in the Precambrian rocks of central England (*see* Figure 3) and parts of Wales.

Since the Precambrian, continuing major continental movements first created and then dispersed a single giant supercontinent, known as Pangaea (Figure 23). This single continent formed a vast landmass, the assembly and dispersal of which has left a marked imprint upon Britain's geological record. During this time, the crust on which 'Britain' was situated drifted northwards as a result of plate movements (Figure 24).

The Cambrian, Ordovician and Silurian rocks of Britain

Rocks of the Cambrian Period, found in Scotland, originally formed part of a North American continent, and were separated from the Cambrian rocks of England and Wales by a wide ocean, the Iapetus (*see* Figure 23a). The fossil record of these rocks includes trilobites, a now extinct group of arthropods, graptolites (*see* Figure

Figure 22. *Precambrian rocks. **(a)** The oldest-known rocks in Britain: the Lewisian Gneiss, in the north-west Highlands of Scotland. Some of these rocks were formed about 3,300 million years ago, in the Precambrian Era. Photo: R. Threadgould.* **(b)** *The Precambrian-age rocks at South Stack, Angelsey were deformed more than once. Photo: S. Campbell.*

39) squid-like nautiloids and other types of mollusc, demonstrating that there was a wide range of animal life in this ocean. The Iapetus Ocean reached its greatest width early in the Ordovician Period and later began to narrow. Enormous thicknesses of muddy sandstones were deposited on the margins

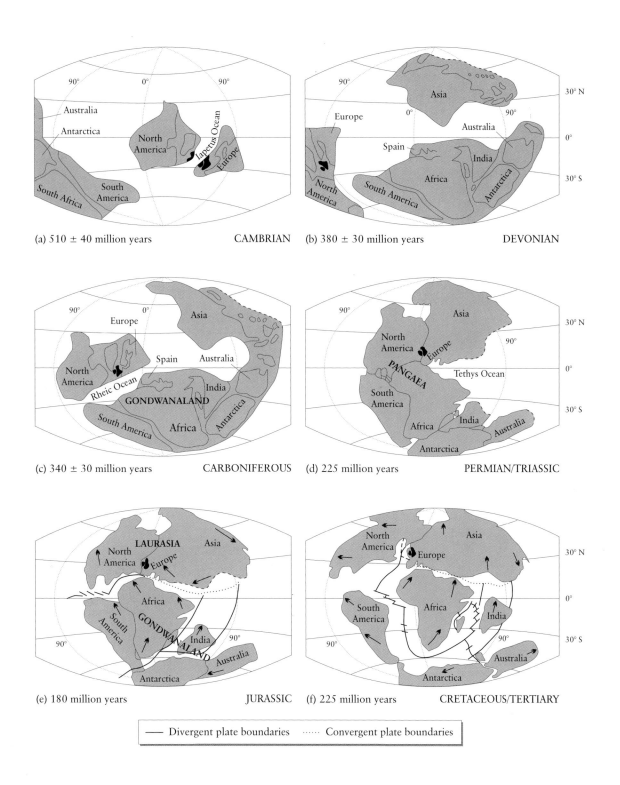

(a) 510 ± 40 million years　　　　CAMBRIAN

(b) 380 ± 30 million years　　　　DEVONIAN

(c) 340 ± 30 million years　　　　CARBONIFEROUS

(d) 225 million years　　　　PERMIAN/TRIASSIC

(e) 180 million years　　　　JURASSIC

(f) 225 million years　　　　CRETACEOUS/TERTIARY

—— Divergent plate boundaries ⋯⋯ Convergent plate boundaries

Figure 23. *Continental drift. Simplified maps illustrating how the continents were distributed during Earth history, indicating the locations of the different parts (dark shading) which have come together to form present-day Britain. After Wyllie (1976).*

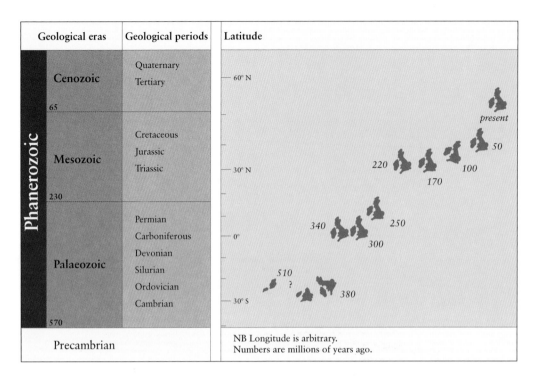

Geological eras	Geological periods	Latitude
Cenozoic 65	Quaternary Tertiary	60° N
Mesozoic 230	Cretaceous Jurassic Triassic	30° N
Palaeozoic 570	Permian Carboniferous Devonian Silurian Ordovician Cambrian	0° 30° S
Precambrian		NB Longitude is arbitrary. Numbers are millions of years ago.

Phanerozoic (vertical label)

Figure 24. *The changing latitude of Britain through geological time. After Lovell (1977).*

of the ocean. As the ocean narrowed, arcs of volcanic islands developed in the 'Lake District' (Figure 25) and 'North Wales'. Mountain building began in Scotland at this time.

Later, in the Silurian Period, the development of coral reefs indicates a shallowing of the ocean. The Silurian fossils show none of the geographic differences characteristic of the Cambrian and Ordovician periods, because by this time species could move freely between either side of the shrinking Iapetus Ocean. At the end of the Silurian, the climax of the Caledonian period of mountain building occurred as 'Scotland' and 'England' finally collided.

The Devonian and Carboniferous rocks of Britain

The Caledonian mountains were rapidly eroded and great thicknesses of sediment, now known as the Old Red Sandstone, accumulated over much of northern 'Britain' and south 'Wales' during the Devonian Period. In 'Devon' and 'Cornwall' the land was bordered by tropical seas which persisted through the Devonian and Carboniferous periods (*see* Figure 23).

The Devonian continent supported freshwater lakes with many fish species. Sediments which formed near hot mineral-rich springs at lake edges,

about 370 million years ago, have been found at Rhynie in Scotland (*see* Figure 46). These contain the remains of the oldest-known higher plants in the world. Insect and arachnid fossils are also found here, demonstrating that the land was being colonised rapidly at that time.

During the early part of the Carboniferous Period the remnants of the Caledonian mountains were flooded by a warm tropical sea in which thick layers of limestone were deposited. In the late Carboniferous huge deltas invaded this sea. On the surface of the deltas dense forests of giant horsetails, tree-ferns, giant clubmosses flourished. The remains of these trees were sometimes buried, to be transformed later into coal (Figure 26). Dragonflies, with a wing span of up to 60 centimetres, and other insects and arthropods were common in these forests, and the first amphibian-like reptile fossils, which are about 340 million years old (Figure 27), have been found in Carboniferous rocks in Scotland.

Towards the end of the Carboniferous Period, a northward-moving plate collided with the southern margin of the Old Red Sandstone Continent in south-west 'England'. This was the final event in the construction of the supercontinent Pangaea (*see* Figure 23c) some 300 million years ago, and caused the Variscan Orogeny (Figure 28). The granites of south-west England were intruded at this time.

Figure 25. *Typical Lake District scenery in the Borrowdale Volcanic Group. The succession of rocks between the Langdale Pikes and Silver Howe represent a six kilometre thickness of volcanic lava and ash, erupted over a period of ten million years during the Ordovician Period. Photo: F. W. Dunning.*

Figure 26. *Carboniferous environments.* **(a)** *A coal-bearing sequence exposed in Duckmanton Railway Cutting, Derbyshire; the dark band is a coal seam. Photo: English Nature.* **(b)** *Reconstruction of the tropical forest of northern England during the Carboniferous Period. During this time, much of 'Britain' was covered by such forests and swamps. It is from the remnants of these forests that much of Britain's coal reserves are derived. A: a lycopod; B: a cycad; C: the horsetail* Calamites; *D:* Boltonites. *Reproduced from Duff et al. (1985).*

Figure 27. *East Kirkton, Lothian, Scotland: amphibians and a possible first reptile (shown in the left foreground). The limestone and shale exposures here, which are of Lower Carboniferous age, are very rich in fossils. The site is a disused limestone quarry. The quarry was abandoned in the middle of the last century and its palaeontological significance has been realised only recently. The nature of the limestone and its restricted distribution (600 metres across and less than ten metres thick) indicates that it may have accumulated in an area of hot springs caused by volcanic activity. It has yielded important early invertebrate and vertebrate faunas, including the earliest-known harvest spiders, millipedes, scorpions, the oldest complete amphibians and the earliest known reptile, Westlothiana lizziae, nicknamed 'Lizzie'. Reconstruction © M. I. Coates. First published in Clarkson et al. (1994). Photo: P. A. MacDonald.*

Figure 28. Hartland Point, Devon. These Upper Carboniferous-age rocks were contorted into tight folds, by the Variscan Orogeny. Photo: A. R. Bennett.

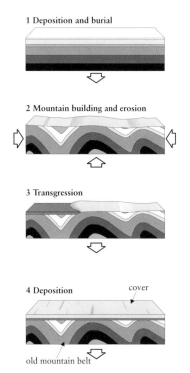

1 Deposition and burial

2 Mountain building and erosion

3 Transgression

4 Deposition

cover

old mountain belt

Figure 29. Sully Island, South Wales. Triassic rocks (230–195 million years old) were formed when 'Britain' lay within the arid belt north of the equator. They lie horizontally on the dipping Carboniferous Limestone. This angular discordance is known as an unconformity, and represents a period of several million years when there was no sediment accumulation. The rocks above the unconformity comprise sands and breccias which are interpreted as lake shore deposits. This site is one of the few places in the world where the margin of a former Triassic lake can be studied. Diagram after Wilson (1994). Photo: C. D. Prosser.

The Permian and Triassic rocks of Britain

Desert conditions prevailed over much of Pangaea during these periods. Vast areas of sand dunes were preserved as the 'New Red Sandstone' (Figure 29). During the Permian Period an inland sea occupied much of the area of what is now the North Sea, and when it began to dry up, evaporite deposits were precipitated (*see* Figure 48).

The drier conditions led to evolutionary changes in the animals and plants. Forests of conifers and cycads (the sago palm is a modern cycad) began to replace the earlier plant-forms, and about 300 million years ago the reptiles became more prolific.

The Jurassic and Cretaceous rocks of Britain

At the beginning of the Jurassic Period much of 'Britain' was flooded by a warm sea teeming with life. In Britain, shallow-

Figure 30. *Jurassic environments.* **(a)** *Plesiosaurs from the early Jurassic based on specimens collected in Gloucestershire which are now housed in Gloucester City Museum.* **(b)** *Scene from mid-Jurassic times, showing a small lake surrounded by seed ferns and conifers based on the fossils from Hornsleasow Quarry, Gloucestershire. Fish* (Lepidotus) *live in the water, and frogs are present at the lake sides. Dinosaurs include some of the earliest stegosaurs and maniraptorans, plated and small carnivorous dinosaurs respectively. A carcass of a large sauropod dinosaur,* Cetiosaurus, *is rotting in the water, and* Megalosaurus *scavenges. Lizard-like animals, crocodiles, pterosaurs, mammals and mammal-like reptiles complete the scene. Paintings by Pam Baldaro. Reproduced by permission of the University of Bristol.*

Figure 31. *The Seven Sisters chalk cliffs in East Sussex. The geomorphology of the cliffs is the result of marine erosion into a series of valleys and intervening ridges. Photo: N. F. Glasser.*

Figure 32. *The Storr, Skye. The photograph shows the landslipped masses of basalt of the Skye Main Lava Series which occupy the foreground. Beyond the Old Man of Storr pinnacle, further lava flows of the Series form left-to-right-dipping scarps. Photo: David Noton Photography.*

marine Jurassic rocks occur in a belt from Dorset to Yorkshire, in South Wales and in scattered patches in the islands of north-west Scotland and in northern Scotland (olive-green in Figure 11). The fossil record of these rocks demonstrates that cephalopods were particularly abundant, especially ammonites and bullet-shaped belemnites. Bivalve and gastropod molluscs, sea urchins and fish were also plentiful. Large marine reptiles such as ichthyosaurs and plesiosaurs were numerous (Figure 30a). The reptiles also flourished on the land and evolved into many forms, including the dinosaurs (Figure 30b). By about 210 million years ago, the first mammals had evolved, and 150 million years ago the first true birds appeared, although they were a relatively insignificant part of the fauna at the time.

Thick deposits of calcareous ooze, formed from the remains of plankton, accumulated in the late Cretaceous seas over much of 'Britain'. These became the Chalk which is now only found in eastern and southern Britain (Figure 31) and Northern Ireland. Towards the end of the Cretaceous Period, sea levels reached an all-time high and most of 'Britain' was submerged beneath the sea.

During the Triassic and Jurassic periods, the supercontinent of Pangaea began to be slowly pulled apart (*see* Figure 23), a process which accelerated in Cretaceous and Tertiary times.

The Tertiary rocks of Britain

The fossil record indicates that many plants and animals became extinct at the Cretaceous–Tertiary boundary about 65 million years ago. This mass extinction was perhaps the result of a global catastrophic event, such as a meteorite impact or major volcanic eruption. On land the dinosaurs and pterosaurs became extinct, but in the Tertiary Period the mammals diversified and flowering plants began to predominate at the expense of the earlier plant types. In the sea, gastropods and bivalve molluscs proliferated, but the ammonites, belemnites and many types of marine reptile became extinct.

As the Atlantic Ocean opened between 'Greenland' and 'Scotland', a chain of volcanoes erupted, flooding the landscape with extensive lava flows. Their eroded remnants can now be recognised on Skye (Figure 32), Rum, Mull, the Ardnamurchan Peninsula, Arran and in Antrim. Later, 'Africa' collided with 'Europe' to form the Alps. The effects of this mountain building episode can be seen in the fold structures of southern Britain (*see* Figure 14).

'Britain' continued to move northwards from the tropics into the cooler mid-latitudes (*see* Figure 24).

Quaternary sediments and landforms of Britain

The long geological history of Britain has influenced its landscape, but much of its present shape was fashioned during the Quaternary Period ('Great Ice Age'), during the last two million years or so. The Quaternary consisted of several ice ages separated by temperate interglacial climates. During the ice ages, glaciers grew in the mountains and occasionally large ice sheets advanced into lowland 'Britain'. On one occasion, ice extended as far south as 'London' (Figure 33).

Early in the Quaternary Period, these ice ages occurred about every 41,000 years, when the uplands of England, Scotland and Wales were probably entirely ice-capped on each occasion, although the evidence has been destroyed by later glaciations. Over the last 900,000 years, however, the rhythm of the major ice ages changed and they have occurred about every 100,000 years. It was during this time that major glaciations greatly modified the landscapes of Britain (Figure 34). As well as eroding deep valleys, the ice sheets deposited clays, sands and gravels, producing landforms such as eskers and drumlins, as well as a widespread mantle of boulder clay ('till') across parts of the country (Figure 35).

Areas beyond the ice-sheet margins were affected by frost, ice and wind, in a cold and dry climate, like the Arctic of today. Such conditions are called 'periglacial'. Slopes were attacked by freezing and thawing processes to create rock debris and produce a widespread layer of periglacial deposits. Rivers were unable to transport all of this material, so deposition occurred on wide floodplains with braided channels. Extensive periglacial gravel deposits are widespread in southern England.

During the ice ages, global sea levels were relatively low because ocean water was locked up in the ice sheets. For example, at the peak of the last ice age, some 22,000 years ago, the sea level was approximately 120 metres below that of today. Thus, 'England' was joined to 'Europe' at that time.

In the glaciated areas of Britain, the weight of the ice depressed the Earth's crust. When the ice retreated, and before the crust 'rebounded' to its former position, the sea fashioned shorelines at

Outer limits of ice cover during glaciations
- Late Devensian   Ridgacre
- Early Devensian   Bristol–Scilly Islands
- Loch Lomond   Anglian

Figure 33. *Ice margins of British glaciations. The ages of these ice advances are:*

- ❏ *Loch Lomond Advance, 11,600 to 12,800 years ago*
- ❏ *Late Devensian glaciations ('the last glaciation'), 23,000 years ago*
- ❏ *Early Devensian Glaciation, about 60,000 years ago*
- ❏ *Ridgacre Glaciation (West Midlands), 160,000 years ago*
- ❏ *Anglian Glaciation, 450,000 years ago*
- ❏ *Bristol-Scilly Islands Glaciation, about 640,000 years ago.*

Figure 34. *Upland glaciation, Snowdonia, Wales. The photograph shows a series of cirques. A cirque is an armchair-shaped hollow, with a steep rock wall at the rear, and a lip or threshold at the front. The rock head wall is fashioned first by weathering and rockfall processes, whereas the floor of the basin is eroded and moulded by glaciers which occupied the hollow. Where two cirques meet, a precipitous divide called an arête develops (to the right in the photograph). Photo: S. Campbell.*

levels relatively lower than at the present. When the crust finally returned to its pre-glacial level, such shorelines were uplifted above present-day sea level to form 'rebound' raised beaches. There are many such beaches in Scotland (*see* Figure 10).

Ice-age conditions were separated by periods of temperate interglacial climate, when Britain was sometimes at least as warm as today, and mixed oak temperate forests became established. During the interglacials there was less ice on the Earth's surface and beaches formed at times of relatively high sea level. These are now found in southern Britain. Many have been raised by gradual long-term uplift.

The flora and fauna of Britain responded to the climatic changes during the Quaternary Period. Variations in the type and distribution of plants and animals have been reconstructed from fossil remains, including pollen grains and fossil bones preserved in peat bogs, as well as lake and cave sediments. This is evident at sites such as West Runton, Norfolk, for example (Figure 36).

Fossils of mammals such as hippopotamus, rhinoceros, elephant, cave hyena, woolly mammoth and early humans have been found in Britain. In the raised beach deposits at Boxgrove, West Sussex, hominid remains (a tibia bone and a tooth) and stone tools have been estimated at between 400,000 and half a million years old. At Swanscombe, in Kent, a skull intermediate in form between *Homo erectus* and Neanderthal Man has been found in sediments about 400,000 years old. Stone tools of an even older age have also been found at High Lodge, Suffolk, and Torquay, Devon.

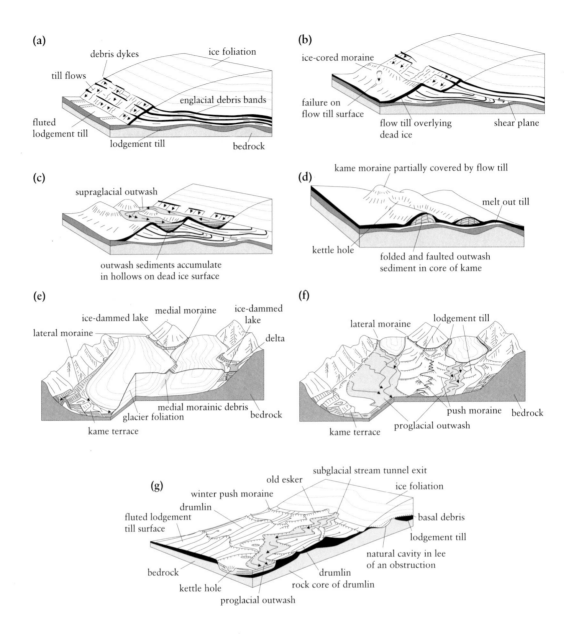

Figure 35. *Schematic diagrams showing the formation of glacial depositional landforms and deposits.* **(a)** *Flow tills form on the surface of the retreating glacier from thick sequences of englacial debris.* **(b)** *Till cover inhibits melting of underlying ice which is left behind during glacier retreat as an ice-cored moraine ridge. Supraglacial flow till is still active.* **(c)** *Outwash from the active glacier is forced to flow between ice-cored ridges and tills flow into the outwash systems. When the outwash dries up, the flow till forms a capping.* **(d)** *Dead ice melts, thus reversing the topography and leaving melt-out till in its place. The kame sediments show collapse structures. Such sequences are extremely common in lowland Britain.* **(e)** *and* **(f)** *Development of the features of a glaciated valley. The principal features are lateral and medial moraines and kame terraces.* **(g)** *The formation of the subglacial/proglacial sediment features. The till surface bears drumlins and on it are superimposed fluted moraine ridges; push-moraine ridges are associated with readvance of the glacier front, either in winter during a general retreat phase or in response to longer term cooling; lee-side till forms in a natural cavity where debris falls from the ice roof. Relatively rare eskers form in subglacial or englacial stream channels; proglacial outwash cuts through the till; kettle holes form in old outwash where stagnant ice blocks melt-out (the underlying sediments show collapse structures). A simple stratigraphy of outwash on till is produced by a single glacial episode of advance and retreat. After Boulton and Paul (1976).*

Britain after the last ice age

Following the disappearance of the last upland glaciers from Britain 11,500 years ago, a succession of vegetation communities recolonised the land and geomorphological processes continued to modify the landscape. On the coast, erosion and deposition caused by variations in the relative level of land and sea as well as the variability of coastal processes, led to changes in the shape of coastlines. Beaches, dune systems and shingle structures also developed where there was a ready supply of sediment. Inland, slopes left after the ice had melted were affected by mass-movement processes, from soil-creep to landslides, while rivers cut channels through the glacial, and other, sediments on valley floors.

The water released to the oceans from the melting of ice sheets in Eurasia and North America flooded any connection between Ireland and Britain. Britain also became separated from continental Europe. At that point, further natural colonisation of plants and animals from the continent was inhibited.

Changes in vegetation over the last 11,500 years are shown by pollen and other plant remains preserved in bogs and lake deposits. The sequence of sediments at such sites can also be used to infer changing environmental conditions and to provide baseline information against which past and present human impacts on the environment may be assessed.

Present-day Britain

Contemporary geomorphological processes cause changes that are, perhaps, not as dramatic as they were during the ice ages. But coastal and river processes can cause major changes over only a few centuries, or even catastrophically, as in the case of the Exmoor floods and North Sea storm-surge flooding, both in 1953. Other examples of geomorphological activity today include weathering and mass-movement processes.

British landscapes have been further diversified by human activity, which has modified slopes and rivers, and provided a cultural overlay of a series of landscapes altered over many historical periods. Historically, perhaps the greatest changes have been those of marsh and heath reclamation, woodland clearance and the development of agricultural field systems.

Figure 36. *West Runton, Norfolk. Sediments exposed in the cliff and on the foreshore accumulated during two interglacials and three ice ages. Fossil pollen indicating the presence of temperate forests has been obtained from the interglacial deposits, while the ice-age deposits show permafrost structures and subarctic herb floras. The dark band at the bottom of the cliff is the 'Freshwater Bed', deposited by a river. Photo: N.F. Glasser.*

THE IMPORTANCE OF BRITAIN IN THE DEVELOPMENT OF GEOLOGY

The record of Earth history has been assembled by the careful accumulation and consideration of evidence from the Earth's rocks. British natural historians, scientists and scholars played a pioneering role in developing the sciences of geology and geomorphology. The wealth of evidence in Britain's landscape enabled them to develop their ideas and theories. A brief account of the early development of geological science is given here to show how important Britain's Earth heritage was in developing the principles of geology.

During the latter part of the eighteenth and the early part of the nineteenth centuries, major advances in geology occurred. In 1795, James Hutton published *Theory of the Earth*, which is

Figure 37. *Hutton's Unconformity at Siccar Point, Berwickshire, is one of the most famous and important geological localities in the world. The section at Siccar Point shows upturned Silurian sediments overlain by sediments from the Old Red Sandstone. The unconformity surface which separates these two sets of rocks represents a significant break in the continuity of the geological record. The portrait of James Hutton by Sir Henry Raeburn (detail) is reproduced by permission of the Scottish National Portrait Gallery. Photograph reproduced by permission of the Director, British Geological Survey. NERC copyright reserved.*

regarded as the first concerted attempt to explain geological phenomena in scientific rather than biblical terms. Hutton defined the principle of uniformitarianism, which is the proposal that processes observed today can be used to interpret the past. He recognised the operation of processes over long periods of geological time and cycles in Earth history (Figure 37). Some of his ideas were developed by John Playfair in his *Illustrations of the Huttonian Theory of the Earth* (1802). Playfair used British examples, particularly relating to the *gradual*, fluvial origins of valleys, a novel concept at a time when catastrophic theory (based on the biblical flood in *Genesis*) dominated. Hutton's work was later developed by Charles Lyell, an immensely influential figure. In *The Principles of Geology*

(1830), he provided a theoretical basis for geology by applying the principles of uniformitarianism.

In 1807 the Geological Society of London was founded, the first geological society in the world. It became a centre for geologists to meet to discuss new discoveries and theories. Not long afterwards, in 1815, William Smith, a land surveyor and civil engineer, published a geological map of England and Wales, based on principles developed from his early observations around Bath, including canal excavations. There he established a system of correlating rock strata by comparing their fossil contents. This became the basis of modern stratigraphy. He was described by the President of the Geological Society, at an award ceremony in 1831, as 'the father of English geology'.

▲ Sir Roderick
Impey Murchison

Adam Sedgwick ▶

Figure 38. *Lummaton Hill Quarry Site of Special Scientific Interest, Torquay, Devon. The rocks exposed in the quarry are massive limestones which were deposited in the later part of the Middle Devonian Period (the Givetian Stage). The limestone contains shell-rich pockets seen here in the upper part of the face. This locality is of great historical importance because the rich faunas it has yielded were used, in part, to characterise the original Devonian System of the pioneering geologists Sedgwick and Murchison. Portraits reproduced with permission of the Director, British Geological Survey. NERC copyright reserved. Photo: K. N. Page.*

In 1835 the Geological Survey of Great Britain was established, the first in the world, to carry out detailed geological mapping of the whole country. Its first Director, Sir Henry de la Beche, produced the first survey memoir, describing the metalliferous ore fields of south-west England. In 1837 the Survey was given accommodation in London, which included a Museum of Practical Geology. In 1934 the museum relocated to South Kensington, where it now forms the Earth Galleries of the Natural History Museum.

In the 1830s, Sir Roderick Impey Murchison began a study of the rocks of south and central Wales. He compared rocks at different localities by means of the fossils they contained, including different species of trilobite. In 1858 he published *Siluria*, naming this sequence of rocks after an ancient Celtic tribe, the Silures. Meanwhile, Adam Sedgwick was investigating the rocks of the Lake District and North Wales. These are older than the rocks that were studied by Murchison and contain

some of the oldest fossils in Britain. He named these rocks the 'Cambrian', based on the Latinised Welsh name for Wales *Cymru*. As a consequence of their further studies in south-west England together they named the Devonian System (Figure 38). Murchison and Sedgwick also discovered fossil fish in the Devonian Old Red Sandstone of Scotland. These finds were added to by Hugh Miller and Louis Agassiz, who were able to portray the nature of the freshwater fish of the Old Red Sandstone.

Although some Cambrian and Silurian rocks as originally defined by Murchison and Sedgwick were quite distinct, others contained similar assemblages of fossils. A controversy erupted between them which was not resolved until after their deaths. Subsequently, Charles Lapworth, a clergyman, spent his spare time studying the rocks around Galashiels in southern Scotland. He looked particularly at graptolite fossils (Figure 39). In comparing his findings with those of Murchison

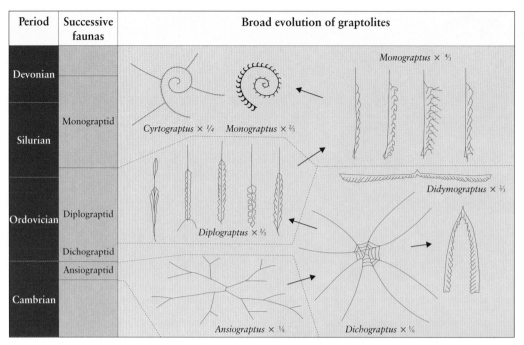

Period	Successive faunas	Broad evolution of graptolites
Devonian		
Silurian	Monograptid	
Ordovician	Diplograptid	
	Dichograptid	
Cambrian	Ansiograptid	

Cyrtograptus × ¼   Monograptus × ⅔

Monograptus × ⅓

Diplograptus × ⅔

Didymograptus × ⅔

Ansiograptus × ⅛   *Dichograptus × ⅙*

Figure 39. *Graptolites first become significant in the geological record in the early Ordovician Period, and became extinct in late Carboniferous/early Permian times. They were colonial organisms living near the sea-surface, consisting of one or more branches (stipes). The individuals of the colony lived in cups along the stipe. Their evolutionary development, as seen in fossils, led to the definition of the Ordovician Period. The photograph shows the graptolite* Didymograptus murchisoni, *from Dyfed, from rocks which are Llanvirn in age (between 455 and 470 million years ago). Photo: G. Larwood. Diagram after Rickards (1993).*

and Sedgwick, he concluded that the overlapping strata were sufficiently distinct to represent a separate period, thereby resolving the earlier controversy. He named this the Ordovician, after the Ordovices, another Celtic tribe which inhabited part of Wales. Thus the Cambrian, Ordovician, Silurian and Devonian Periods were all named in Britain.

In the 1820s Mary Anning collected and sold Jurassic fossils in Lyme Regis, Dorset (Figure 40). She discovered remarkably complete specimens of the marine reptile *Ichthyosaurus*; the first-known articulated skeleton was discovered by her when she was a girl of eleven. She also found the first almost complete *Plesiosaurus* skeleton in 1823 and remains of the flying reptile *Dimorphodon* in 1828. These finds proved to be important for the study and interpretation of the evolution of reptiles.

In 1822, Mary Ann Mantell discovered fossil teeth in the Cretaceous Wealden rocks while walking in Ashdown Forest, Sussex. These were later identified as those of a large herbivorous reptile, *Iguanodon*. In 1824, a fossil thigh bone came into the hands of Professor William Buckland, who named the animal *Megalosaurus*, later discovered to be a large carnivore. Further finds included fossils of the armoured *Hylaeosaurus*, described by Charles Mantell (Mary Ann's husband) in 1832, and a large sauropod dinosaur, *Cetiosaurus*, from the Oxford Clay near

Figure 40. *The Jurassic rocks of the cliffs near Lyme Regis and portrait of Mary Anning. Portrait reproduced by permission of The Natural History Museum, London. Photo: P. Doyle.*

Peterborough. In 1841, at a meeting of the British Association for the Advancement of Science, Dr Richard Owen first suggested that *Iguanodon, Megalosaurus* (*see* Figure 43) and *Hylaeosaurus* should together be called the Dinosauria. Thus it was the discoveries of British fossil reptiles which led to the naming of this group.

Significant advances in the understanding of ice ages and landscape changes were also made in Britain during the nineteenth century. In the early 1840s the evidence of glacial landforms in Scotland made a significant impression on the Swiss geologist Louis Agassiz, a leading figure in advancing 'the Glacial Theory'. He helped develop thinking on the possibility of glaciation in areas where there were no modern glaciers. In 1842 Charles Darwin and William Buckland also confirmed the ideas of Agassiz in Wales. Robert Jamieson and Charles Maclaren played an important part in the wider dissemination of the ideas Agassiz advocated, together with those of other early glacialists.

Maclaren is also credited with first recognising the sea-level changes associated with glacio-eustasy (changes in global sea level as water, once locked up in ice sheets, was released on subsequent melting). Thomas Jamieson was the first to recognise complementary glacio-isostatic changes in sea level ('rebound' of continental crust when the weight of ice which depressed it is removed upon melting of the ice). His conclusion was based on detailed studies of raised beach deposits in the Forth Valley.

Archibald Geikie, Director General of the Geological Survey, Andrew Ramsay and James Croll identified multiple phases of glaciation in the sedimentary record. Croll also recognised that the changes in climate were controlled by variations in the Earth's orbit around the Sun and that ocean currents played a major part in heat transfer from the tropics to higher latitudes. Geikie contributed significantly to the understanding and interpretation of the links between geology and geomorphology. His younger brother, James, published *The Great Ice Age* in 1874, a highly influential book with an international perspective on the Ice Age.

During the nineteenth and twentieth centuries the Geological Society of London, the British Geological Survey and the universities, amongst others, advanced the study of geology and geomorphology in Great Britain. Knowledge of the geological column has been refined by international collaboration, which has also facilitated the correlation of geological events in Britain with those elsewhere. At the same time, our understanding of the geological and geomorphological processes which have been at work throughout the period of geological history continues to be deepened, and methods for locating economic resources below ground also continue to be developed and refined.

Chapter 4

The Geological Conservation Review

In a country such as Britain, with a relatively small land area and a population of over 55 million, there are many demands on land that may conflict with site conservation. There is a demand for hard rock and sand and gravel to meet the requirements of the construction industry, as well as clay for bricks, limestone for cement, and landfill sites for waste disposal. Just as it is impracticable to conserve every rock exposure, it is essential to conserve those that make a unique contribution to Britain's Earth heritage. The identification of those sites that need to be conserved has been the purpose of the Geological Conservation Review.

From the late 1940s until the late 1970s, the identification of the most important Earth heritage sites was undertaken by the Nature Conservancy (1949–1973) and then the Nature Conservancy Council (1973–1991) on the basis of available information and the advice of Earth scientists.

The launch of the Geological Conservation Review in 1977 marked a more systematic approach to site selection. The objective of the review was to identify those sites needed to show all the key scientific elements of the Earth heritage of Britain. Site selection was undertaken between 1977 and 1990 by the Nature Conservancy Council. It covered both the geology and geomorphology of Britain and involved several hundred scientists from higher education, government, industry and the voluntary sector. The sites selected were called Geological Conservation Review sites and they form the basis of statutory Earth heritage conservation in Britain. The current responsibility for site selection and deselection rests with the statutory nature conservation agencies: the Countryside Council for Wales, English Nature and Scottish Natural Heritage.

The results of the Geological Conservation Review programme are being published in a series of 42 volumes, each of which provides a public record of the evaluation of each Geological Conservation Review site placed in a national and, where appropriate, international context.

PRINCIPLES OF SITE SELECTION

Aims of the Geological Conservation Review

From the outset, the Geological Conservation Review used the highest scientific standards to identify systematically the key Earth science sites in Britain. The site series would reflect the range and diversity of Great Britain's Earth heritage, and each site would ultimately satisfy the legal requirements for notification as a Site of Special Scientific Interest by reason of its 'geology or physiography' ('physiography' is synonymous with 'geomorphology'). The notification of Sites of Special Scientific Interest under the *National Parks and Access to the Countryside Act 1949* and subsequently under the *Wildlife and Countryside Act 1981*, is the main mechanism of legal protection in Great Britain (*see* information box on page 46).

To achieve these aims, criteria and guidelines were developed. These can be encapsulated in three distinct, but complementary, components:

1   sites of importance to the **international** community of Earth scientists
2   sites that are scientifically important because they contain **exceptional** features
3   sites that are nationally important because they are **representative** of an Earth science feature, event or process which is fundamental to Britain's Earth history.

'Nationally important' in the context of Geological Conservation Review site selection refers to importance to Great Britain as a whole, and means that any site chosen for the Geological Conservation Review has been assessed, wherever possible, against comparable features, where they exist, across the whole of Great Britain.

Each site selected for the Geological Conservation Review is of at least national importance for Earth heritage conservation, and many of the sites are of international importance.

THE FIRST COMPONENT — INTERNATIONAL IMPORTANCE

The first component for Geological Conservation Review site selection ensures that geological and geomorphological sites of international importance are included so that our international responsibilities are met. Five main types of internationally important Geological Conservation Review site can be recognised:

❏   time interval or boundary stratotypes; for example, the boundary stratotype at Pitch Coppice, Herefordshire (Figure 41; *see also* Figure 2)

Sites of Special Scientific Interest (SSSIs)

Since the establishment of government-based conservation agencies in the late 1940s, the identification of a series of discrete sites for protection has become the principal instrument of nature conservation. During the 1980s, attention moved towards more holistic and 'wider countryside' approaches to conservation, and this trend continues. Despite this, site-based conservation remains an indispensable means of protecting specific features of scientific interest. The British SSSI system is a conservation mechanism that confers legal protection on sites.

An SSSI is the designation by law of an area of Britain that is, in the opinion of the statutory agency concerned, of special scientific interest for its flora, fauna, geological or geomorphological features. Such areas may be large or small. The duty to designate an SSSI is vested in the three nature conservation agencies, the Countryside Council for Wales, English Nature and Scottish Natural Heritage. SSSI status provides a mechanism for consultation about threats or activities that may endanger the special interest of a site. Designation of a site as an SSSI does not over-rule existing planning permission.

A similar system operates in Northern Ireland, where designation of a site as an Area of Special Scientific Interest (under the *Nature Conservation and Amenity Lands (Northern Ireland) Order 1985*, as amended by the *Nature Conservation and Amenity Lands (Amendment) (Northern Ireland) Order 1989*) affords a comparable degree of protection.

The series of 3002 Geological Conservation Review sites is likely to become about 2300 Earth science SSSIs when the process of notification is complete (some SSSIs contain more than one Geological Conservation Review site within their boundaries). On average, 400 applications for development or substantial change are made each year across Britain at these sites. Of these proposals, more than 90 would, if carried out, cause deterioration of the Earth science feature of interest at the site, and about 20 would cause serious damage or destruction.

The description or mention of any site, however, should not be taken as an indication that access to a site is open or that a right of way exists. Most sites described in a Geological Conservation Review volume, for example, are in private ownership, and publication of their descriptions is for the purpose of justifying their SSSI status.

Figure 41. *Pitch Coppice, Mortimer Forest, near Ludlow, Herefordshire, is officially recognised by the International Union of Geological Sciences (IUGS) as the global reference site used to define the base of the Gorstian Stage of the Silurian Period. Typical fossils are used to compare this sequence of rock layers with rocks containing the same fossils in other parts of the world, establishing those too as Gorstian in age.*

This stratotype site forms part of a geological trail managed by Forest Enterprise. Vegetation is controlled, and the site remains accessible all year round to visiting scientists, educational groups and interested members of the public. The photograph shows visiting delegates of the Malvern International Conference on Geological and Landscape Conservation (1993). Photo: K. N. Page.

Figure 42. (a) *Aerial view of Wenlock Edge, Shropshire, looking north-eastwards towards Hope Dale (to the right of the photograph). The escarpment is formed mainly by the Farley Member beds capped by the Much Wenlock Limestone Formation. Photo: Cambridge University Collection. Reproduced by permission of the Curator of Aerial Photography.*

(b) *Section of Silurian reef limestones of Wenlock Edge. Wenlock Edge is one of the classic areas of British geology and formed part of the Wenlock type area defined by Sir Roderick Murchison in the first half of the nineteenth century. The detailed stratigraphy has since been investigated and revised. Today it is the designated type area for the Much Wenlock Limestone Formation and it forms part of the international type area for the Wenlock Series.*

Many of the disused limestone quarry faces backing onto Wenlock Edge are now buried beneath extensive earth buttresses constructed to reduce the risk of rock collapse, but sections are still available for study. Photo: M. J. Harley.

❑ type localities for biozones (rock strata which are characterised by a closely defined fossil content, usually a fossil species) and chronozones (rock strata formed during the time-span of the relevant stratotypes) (Figure 42)

❑ internationally significant type localities for particular rock types, mineral or fossil species (e.g. the fossil reptile *Megalosaurus* from Stonesfield in the Cotswolds, Figure 43), and outstanding landform examples such as Chesil Beach (*see* Figure 45)

❑ historically important type localities where rock or time units were first described or characterised, or where great advances in geological theory were first made (e.g.

Hutton's Unconformity at Siccar Point, Berwickshire (*see* Figure 37)

❑ important localities where geological or geomorphological phenomena were first recognised and described, or where a principle or concept was first conceived or demonstrated (e.g. cauldron subsidence at Glencoe; Figure 44).

THE SECOND COMPONENT — EXCEPTIONAL FEATURES

Many sites have unique, rare or special features (Figure 45). For example, at Rhynie in Scotland, a mineralised peat, in the form of a siliceous rock called chert (Figure

Figure 43. *Type specimen of* Megalosaurus bucklandi *Meyer, 1832. Partial lower jaw. Stonesfield is the most important of the British Bathonian localities in the Cotswolds, and arguably the best Middle Jurassic terrestrial reptile site in the world. Its fauna is diverse and abundant, and consists of more than 15 species of fossil reptile, including turtles, crocodilians, pterosaurs, dinosaurs and rare marine forms (ichthyosaurs, plesiosaurs), as well as mammal-like*

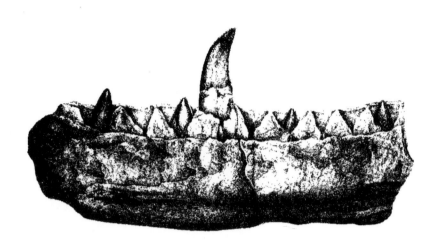

reptiles and mammals. Stonesfield is the most important site in the world for remains of Megalosaurus. *It yielded the 'type' material in the early nineteenth century, and continued to produce hundreds of specimens while the mines were in operation. Diagram after Buckland (1824).*

Figure 44. *Glencoe, Lochaber. This dramatic glaciated glen has particular historical significance as the place where 'cauldron subsidence' was first recognised in 1909. Volcanologists had long been intrigued by certain collapse features of volcanoes and many workers had been actively seeking to explain their origin.*

It was an officer of the Scottish Geological Survey, Edward Bailey, who, within days of visiting Glencoe, attributed the beautifully exposed collapse features to a mechanism he termed cauldron subsidence. Bailey was so excited about his findings that he travelled directly to the Geological Society in London and made an impromptu presentation about the Glencoe rocks.

Evidence for cauldron subsidence is now preserved in five localities within the SSSI. As Glencoe was the first example of this phenomenon to be described in any detail, it serves as the type example throughout the world.

Recent research, mostly concerned with establishing links between the sequence of volcanic eruptions at the surface and the development of igneous intrusions deep in the Earth's crust, has further reinforced interest in the area and its international importance. Photo: P. A. MacDonald.

Figure 45. *Chesil Beach, Dorset, is a site of international importance for the impressive and exceptional size of its storm beach, the systematic sorting by size of the cobbles and pebbles along the shore, and the availability of historical records of beach changes. It is an active coastal geomorphological site. Together with Orfordness and Dungeness, it is one of only three major shingle structures on the coast of England.*

The 29-kilometre shingle beach is joined to the mainland at the eastern and western ends, but for 13 kilometres it is backed by the Fleet, a shallow brackish lagoon. The pebble beach consists almost entirely (98%) of flint derived from the Chalk. The remainder is composed of chert and quartzite (both resistant rocks) derived from outside the region. The precursor of Chesil Beach probably existed some 125,000 years ago as a shingle bank well offshore from the present beach. The formation of the present Chesil Beach took place between about 15,000 and 5000 years ago, when rapidly rising sea levels caused the erosion of gravel-rich deposits and wave action drove the coarse material onshore as a barrier beach. Photograph reproduced by permission of the Director, British Geological Survey. NERC copyright reserved.

46), of Devonian age, preserves a detailed record of an early land ecosystem. The exceptional microscopic detail preserved in the Rhynie fossils makes this site quite exceptional. No other sites are known in Britain to contain such well-preserved material of this age. This makes Rhynie irreplaceable. The inclusion of exceptional sites ensures that the highlights of British geology and geomorphology are conserved.

Exceptional sites may be visually striking and can contribute dramatically to the character of the landscape, for instance, Haytor Rocks on Dartmoor (*see* Figure 1), Cheddar Gorge, Somerset, and Chesil Beach, Dorset. In contrast, the unremarkable appearance of East Kirkton Quarry belies the extraordinary character of the fossil assemblage it contains (*see* Figure 27).

THE THIRD COMPONENT — REPRESENTATIVENESS

Important though international and exceptional sites are, they cannot provide the basis for a systematic approach to the selection of sites to cover the essential features of the Earth heritage of Britain. This is provided by the selection of sites representative of features, events and processes that are fundamental to our understanding of the geological history of Britain. The starting point of the review was to create subject 'blocks' which provided an overall structure for site selection (the list of blocks can be found at the end of this chapter). This ensured that the different themes of Earth science would receive comparable treatment. The second stage in this approach was to consider the characteristic features of each block and to select representative sites. Within individual blocks, sites fall into natural groupings based upon geological features or scenarios. These groups are now referred to as networks and there may be one or more networks in any block.

GEOLOGICAL CONSERVATION REVIEW BLOCKS

Many of the Geological Conservation Review blocks correspond to the standard divisions of geological time or to major events within those periods. They can be grouped into seven broad categories:

Figure 46. *Rhynie Chert. The site at Rhynie in Scotland is visually unimpressive, and may seem an unlikely geological location, but it is one of the most important palaeontological sites in Great Britain and the world. The Rhynie site contains some of the finest preserved and earliest land plants* (Devonian) *in the world. It also contains the earliest-known wingless insect* (Rhyniella) *and one of the finest Devonian micro-arthropod faunas in the world, including mites, springtails and a*

small aquatic shrimp-like organism, Lepidocaris.

The fossils are preserved in chert. The deposit is an excellent example of the freak preservation of life resulting from the flooding of a marsh surface on which these plants were growing, by silica-rich water originating from a hot spring. The hot water killed and preserved the plants and animals before their tissues decayed, and so preserved a complete ecosystem.

The arthropods found in the deposit are all primitive forms, and show an early association between plants and their parasites. Preservation is so good that microscopic damage to the plants by these arthropods is seen, as are invading fungal hyphae. The plants are preserved so well that thin sections of rock can be sliced, and examined under a microscope, to reveal the cell structure, including the minute detail of spores as well as cell xylem and stomata.

The photographs show a sample and thin section of the chert. The thin section shows the mouthparts of a palaeocharinid (a spider-like arthropod). Photos: C. C. J. MacFadyen (chert sample) and N. H. Trewin (thin section).

❏   stratigraphy (35 blocks)
❏   palaeontology (16 blocks)
❏   Quaternary geology (16 blocks)
❏   geomorphology: the landforms and processes that form the current landscape (10 blocks)
❏   igneous petrology (6 blocks)
❏   structural and metamorphic geology (10 blocks)
❏   mineralogy (7 blocks)

Stratigraphy blocks

For the most part, these blocks are classified according either to their stratigraphical age (stage, period) or to a range of stratigraphical ages (e.g. Caradoc–Ashgill Block). Blocks for some stratigraphical ages, however, were defined not purely by age, but also by geographical area or environmental setting where there were significant variations in the rocks across

Britain formed at the same time. This is why there are two blocks for the Devonian Period, one for marine rocks and one for non-marine rocks.

It is not possible in every case to define blocks by stratigraphical age. For example, where fossils are rare or absent it is difficult to locate the boundary between different geological ages. Such stratigraphical units are named after the geographical localities where they were defined, for example, the Wealden Group consists of mudstone, shale and sandstone that only occur in south-east England.

Most invertebrate fossils (e.g. trilobites, echinoderms, ammonites and other molluscs) are also addressed within the stratigraphy blocks, since these fossils are widely used in correlating rock strata. Because of the relative rarity of fossils such as reptiles, fish, mammals, birds, terrestrial plants, insects and other arthropods (excluding trilobites), these are covered in separate palaeontology blocks.

Palaeontology blocks

These blocks address the evolution and diversity of significant animal and plant groups not included in the stratigraphy blocks (*see* above) and therefore have independent block status. Geological time is used as the basis to define some blocks, for example, Jurassic–Cretaceous Reptilia.

Quaternary blocks

The Quaternary blocks are classified on a *regional* basis, although the subdivision of time (usually stratigraphical age) is an important factor. Sites were selected to represent the stratigraphy of Quaternary successions and the development of landforms.

During the Quaternary Period, northern Britain was covered by a succession of ice sheets, while southernmost Britain was not glaciated, although frozen ground conditions were experienced. The wide variation of stratigraphical units and geomorphological features across Britain, and the large number of sites available for study, required that a topic classification for networks within these blocks was adopted. Three principal themes form the basis of the Geological Conservation Review Quaternary site selection:

❑ *environmental history and change* based on the stratigraphy at different localities, age and fossil content, e.g. glacial-interglacial history, sea-level changes
❑ *processes and patterns of landscape evolution*, e.g. glaciation, periglaciation
❑ *the history and development of the flora and fauna*, e.g. vegetation history, evolution of vertebrates.

Comparisons were made between the regional Quaternary blocks to ensure that certain categories of site were not over-represented.

Geomorphology blocks

Geomorphology blocks cover the history and development of landforms and geomorphological processes active today, for example, rivers, coasts and landslides. Unlike geological sites where processes can only be inferred, active geomorphological sites provide open-air laboratories where processes can be studied.

Because geomorphology influences landscape and habitat, there is great potential for integrating the physical and biological components of nature conservation in geomorphological sites.

Igneous petrology and structural and metamorphic geology blocks

The igneous petrology and structural and metamorphic geology blocks relate to the effects of mountain building activity, such as the Caledonian Orogeny.

Major episodes of igneous activity form the basis of six igneous Geological Conservation Review blocks, and these are linked to mountain building (e.g. South-west England Igneous), and the opening of oceans (e.g. Tertiary Igneous).

Structural blocks relate to the deformation processes during three major mountain building episodes (e.g. the Caledonian, Variscan and Alpine orogenies) and their variation across Britain. These blocks include geological features such as folds and faults, and other effects resulting from compressional and tensional forces acting within the crust of the Earth.

Four blocks relate to Precambrian rocks in Scotland: the Lewisian, Torridonian, Moine and Dalradian Blocks. Three of these, the Lewisian, Moine and Dalradian Blocks, have been deformed and metamorphosed during mountain building.

Figure 47. (a) The palaeogeography of Britain during the late Permian approximately 250 million years ago — an artist's impression of a satellite view. The outline of the present-day coastline of Britain is shown as a dotted line. Much of 'Britain' was desert, with a large inland sea to the east, and a smaller one to the west of the what is now the Pennines, possibly both connected by a sea-way to an open ocean to the north of 'Norway' and 'Greenland'. Reproduced from F.W. Dunning et al. (1978) by permission of the Natural History Museum, London. *(b)* The extent of the late Permian inland sea (the Zechstein Sea). After Smith (1995).

Mineralogy blocks

These blocks address the minerals produced as the result of igneous, metamorphic or sedimentary processes.

GEOLOGICAL CONSERVATION REVIEW NETWORKS

Because the concept of the *network* is fundamental to the methods of the Geological Conservation Review, it is illustrated in some detail in this chapter by describing the actual networks adopted in Geological Conservation Review blocks. To aid understanding, the networks described here have been simplified to some degree, but they indicate the overall approach taken.

MARINE PERMIAN GEOLOGICAL CONSERVATION REVIEW BLOCK

Durham Province network: the western edge of an inland sea

Figure 47a is an artist's impression of a satellite view of the 'British Isles' as they would have looked some 250 million years ago, towards the end of the Permian Period. The climate was arid, much like the Sahara and Arabian

GEOLOGICAL CONSERVATION REVIEW NETWORKS

Two networks represent the Marine Permian Block of Britain:

- Durham Province network (worked example given)

- Yorkshire Province network.

Gulf regions of the present day. Mountainous areas in what is now southern England and Wales had only recently (in geological terms) been uplifted during the Variscan Orogeny, and remnants of the earlier Caledonian mountains persisted in Scotland. Much of the present-day area of the North Sea was occupied by an inland sea (the Zechstein Sea, named after thick Permian rocks deposited in this sea to the east in northern Germany and Poland) which was probably linked to an open ocean to the north through a narrow sea-way between 'Norway' and 'Greenland' (Figure 47b). Sediments accumulated on the western margin of this sea, and those in an even smaller inland sea to the west of what is now the Pennines are referred to as the Marine Permian. One volume of the Geological Conservation Review is devoted to them (Smith, 1995).

When the level of the Zechstein Sea was relatively high, reefs and shallow-water sand banks fringed its margins (Figure 48a). The reefs and banks formed limestone deposits (calcium carbonate), but were altered to dolomite (calcium-magnesium carbonate) soon after deposition. Their outcrop forms a north–south strip across County Durham, Yorkshire and Nottinghamshire, with small outcrops in Cumbria. When the sea level dropped, it seems that the link with the open ocean to the north was severed or reduced, so that evaporation caused the salinity of the Zechstein Sea to increase. This resulted in the deposition of evaporite minerals such as halite (sodium chloride — common salt) and anhydrite (calcium sulphate), seaward of the earlier limestone deposits (Figure 48b).

Five episodes of sea-level highs and lows have been recognised in deposits laid down beneath the Zechstein Sea. These are referred to as Zechstein Cycles, and can be traced from north-east England and under the North Sea into Germany and Poland. Only evidence for the first two and the beginning of the third is exposed at the surface in the County

Durham area. Figure 48c is a west to east cross-section of the area showing the rock units deposited during cycles 1 and 2 and the base of 3. Note that the rock formations composed of evaporite minerals are only known from boreholes to the east of strata exposed at the surface, and are represented at the surface only by the thin residues left after the soluble minerals were dissolved away. The Ford Formation within the first Zechstein Cycle (Figure 48d) is particularly important, as it contains evidence for the development of a reef that fringed the Zechstein Sea. This was not a coral reef. The most abundant fossils found within it are bryozoans (small colonial organisms that build calcareous skeletons) that acted as sediment baffles which trapped the muddy limestone sediments to build the reef edifice. The sediments probably became rapidly hardened (lithified) due to the action of cyano-bacteria and the formation of inorganic carbonate minerals which cemented them, and so would have been able to withstand wave action. However, storm waves would have broken up the reef edge, so that a slope of reef debris built up in front of the reef. An idealised section across the reef and the location of the reef crest are shown in Figure 48d.

Figures 48c and 48d encapsulate the theoretical framework for which sites were selected that illustrate the key geological features of the marine Permian of County Durham. Ideally, sites illustrating all the environmental settings shown in Figures 48a and 48b should be selected for the network. However, it is impossible to find sites showing sediments composed of the evaporite minerals anhydrite and halite at the surface because these minerals are dissolved away. However, sites showing the residues left behind have been selected. The development of a reef of a type very different from those known today adds an extra palaeontological dimension to the theoretical framework, requiring the selection of sites showing successive stages in the growth of the structure. The stratigraphical locations of the sites selected for the Marine Permian Durham Province network are shown in Figures 48c and 48d. Their geographical locations are shown in Figure 49.

Yorkshire Province network

The Yorkshire Province lies to the south of the Cleveland High. The rocks exposed here are the shallow-water shelf deposits grading eastwards (over a distance of about 30 kilometres) into finer-grained carbonates. The

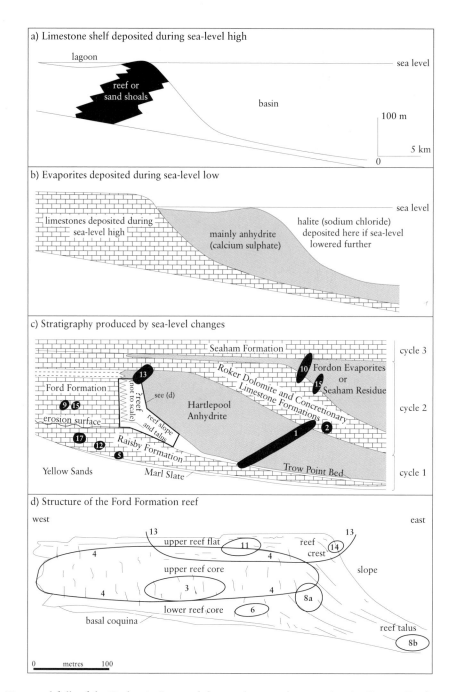

Figure 48. *Rises and falls of the Zechstein Sea and the resultant rock succession in County Durham.*
(a) Deposition of limestone shelves, fringed by reefs, occurred during relative sea-level highs. (b) When the relative sea level dropped, the inland sea was probably partially cut off from the open ocean to the north, so that evaporation raised its salinity resulting in the deposition of evaporite minerals. (c) West to east cross-section showing the distribution of the dolomitised limestone and evaporite formations (and their residues resulting from near-surface dissolution). Cycles 1–3 shown on the right side of the diagram relate to the successive periods of high and low sea level depicted in (a) and (b) which resulted in dolomitised limestone formations being overlain by evaporite formations. The Yellow Sands shown at the base of the diagram were deposited from migrating desert dunes (similar sands in the southern North Sea are important gas reservoirs). The Marl Slate is a shale rich in organic material that was deposited immediately after the Zechstein Sea flooded the North Sea area. The numbers indicate the stratigraphical position of sites listed in the table on page 56. (d) Section showing the structure of the reef within the Ford Formation in Cycle 1. Numbers refer to sites listed in the table.

The distribution of Permian Marine rocks in the Durham Province

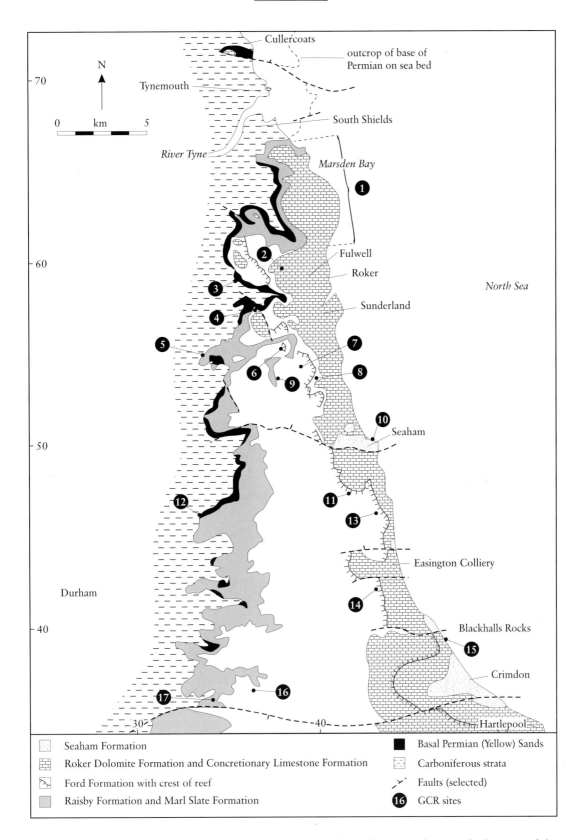

Figure 49. *The distribution of Permian marine rocks in the Durham Province, showing the location of the sites selected for the Geological Conservation Review network for this area. The crest of the Ford Formation reef is shown. After Smith (1995).*

MARINE PERMIAN BLOCK: DURHAM PROVINCE NETWORK

SITE NAME	*GCR SELECTION CRITERIA*
1 Trow Point to Whitburn Bay	Representative of sedimentation along a marine shallow sea margin and the effects of dissolution of evaporites.
2 Fulwell Hills Quarries	Representative of Concretionary Limestone.
3 Hylton Castle Cutting	Representative of lower reef-core of the Ford Formation.
4 Claxheugh Rock, Cutting and Ford Quarry	Representative of section through shelf-edge reef and backreef strata of the Ford Formation.
5 Dawson's Plantation Quarry, Penshaw	Representative of sediment instability in the lower part of the Raisby Formation.
6 Humbledon Hill Quarry	Representative of fauna in the English Zechstein reef. International reference locality for the bryozoan *Stomatopora voigtiana*.
7 Tunstall Hills (North)	Representative of shelf-edge reef-core of the Ford Formation.
8 (a) Tunstall Hills (South) and (b) Ryhope Cutting	Representative of shelf-edge reef-core and talus of the Ford Formation.
9 Gilleylaw Plantation Quarry	Representative of patch-reef and reef-margin sediments of the Ford Formation.
10 Seaham	Representative of strata of the Seaham Formation and Seaham Residue.
11 Stony Cut, Cold Hesledon	Representative of reef flat to reef crest in the Ford Formation.
12 High Moorsley Quarry	Representative of the Magnesian Limestone of the lower part of the Raisby Formation.
13 Hawthorn Quarry	Representative of reef flat of the Ford Formation, Hesleden Dene Stromatolite Biostrome and the overlying Roker Dolomite.
14 Horden Quarry	Representative of crest of shelf-edge reef of the Ford Formation.
15 Blackhalls Rocks	Representative of the Hesleden Dene Stromatolite Biostrome.
16 Trimdon Grange Quarry	Representative of backreef lagoonal sediments of the Ford Formation.
17 Raisby Quarries	Representative of the Raisby Formation.

Yorkshire Province differs from the Durham Province in that the barrier carbonate rocks which were formed near the western edge of the Zechstein Sea during the second main depositional cycle lie too far east to outcrop onshore. The sites selected for the network link together the characteristic types of sedimentation seen in this lagoonal backreef environment of the late Permian in Yorkshire. The outcrops in this province are characterised by lagoonal limestone rocks (which were later converted to dolomite), together with bryozoan–algal patch-reefs. In the north of the Province, examples of features not seen in the Durham Province occur, such as marine sabkha deposits (a sabkha is a wide area of coastal flats bordering a lagoon where evaporite minerals are formed) and a rare exposure of marine evaporites.

Figure 50. *Sequence of diagrams showing igneous processes associated with large-scale crustal movements culminating in the growth of a mountain chain.*
(a) *Igneous intrusions and volcanic rocks prior to mountain building.*
(b) *Generation of magma deep in the crust, and the formation of batholiths.*
(c) *Minor intrusions — dykes, sills — form at the end of the orogeny (see Figure 12).*

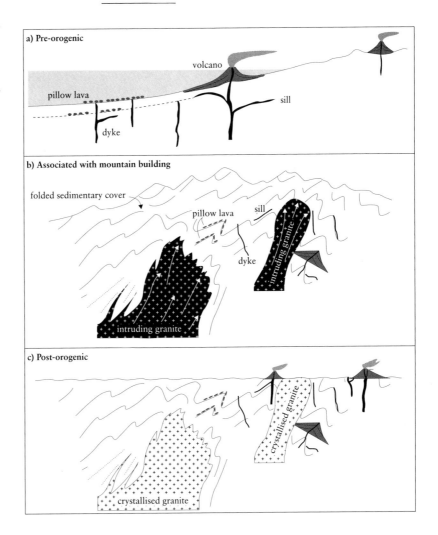

IGNEOUS ROCKS OF SOUTH-WEST ENGLAND GEOLOGICAL CONSERVATION REVIEW BLOCK

GEOLOGICAL CONSERVATION REVIEW NETWORKS

- Pre-orogenic volcanic network
- Cornubian granite batholith network (worked example given)
- Post-orogenic volcanic network
- Lizard and Start complexes network.

There have been many periods of igneous activity during Britain's geological history, including several during the Precambrian, and four main episodes since then, during the Ordovician, Devonian, Carboniferous/Permian and Tertiary periods. Such activity is commonly linked to large-scale movements of the Earth's crust and the resultant plate tectonic activity, as described in Chapter 3.

In those cases where the igneous processes are associated with large-scale crustal movements culminating in the growth of a mountain chain, at least three phases of activity can commonly be identified (Figure 50). The earliest events are associated with volcanic activity and shallow intrusions of molten rock in and around basins where sediments accumulate (Figure 50a). The resulting igneous rocks then become affected by mountain-building processes, and are deformed and occasionally metamorphosed. The second phase of activity involves the generation of large volumes of granitic magma deep in the crust, which then rise through the core of the mountain chain to be intruded at higher levels in the crust (Figure 50b). The final phase of igneous activity occurs

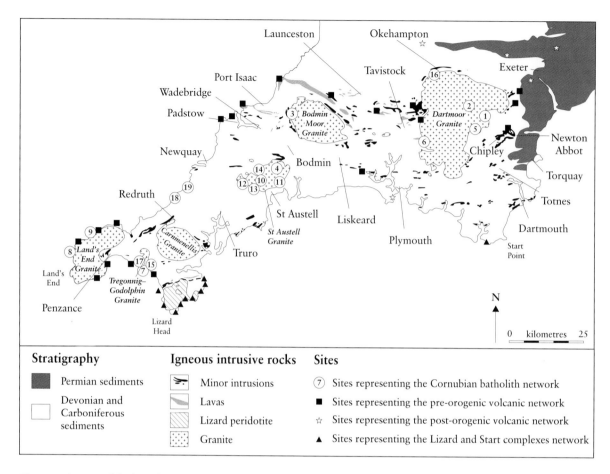

Figure 51. *Simplified geological map of south-west England showing the distribution of igneous rocks and the location of Geological Conservation Review sites. Sites of the Cornubian granite batholith network are numbered as in the site list in the text. After Floyd* et al. *(1993).*

after the main tectonic events are over, and generally involves the development of volcanic activity and minor igneous intrusions (Figure 50c).

The igneous rocks of south-west England (Figure 51) illustrate the range of complex relationships which occurred during the three phases described above of the Variscan Orogeny. This Orogeny occurred about 300 million years ago when south-west England was on the northern margin of the mountain-building area (*see* Figure 17). The core of the mountain chain lay to the south in the Massif Central of France. The sediments which accumulated in south-west England in Devonian and Carboniferous times include volcanic rocks, which now provide the basis of the pre-orogenic volcanic Geological Conservation Review network. Although these rocks were intensely folded and deformed during the orogeny, the amount of metamorphism they underwent was low and the rocks have retained much of their original structure. After the rocks

had been folded they were intruded by a large granitic magma, the characteristics of which are used to create the Cornubian granite batholith Geological Conservation Review network. The granite cut through earlier igneous rocks and fold structures, and so was intruded after the tectonic event. It can be distinguished from other granites which occur to the south, in Brittany and the Massif Central, whose formation was intimately associated with the mountain-building process. This is an example of where a potential network exists, but it is absent from Britain. Following the orogeny, there was a period of minor volcanic activity represented by the post-orogenic volcanic network. South-west England also includes the metamorphosed igneous rock complexes of the Lizard and Start peninsulas. These areas are not directly linked geologically to the networks outlined previously, but as they form a geographical unit are included as the Lizard and Start complexes network.

Pre-orogenic volcanic network

This network comprises those igneous and volcanic rocks which accumulated within the Devonian and Carboniferous sediments prior to the Variscan Orogeny (Figure 51; compare with Figure 50a). The network includes the following geological situations:

❏ different forms of igneous intrusive and extrusive process, such as sills and pillow lavas, and the development of areas characterised by different rock types

❏ variations within individual igneous bodies, including gradations from intrusive to extrusive, and internal zonation in igneous bodies

❏ different relationships between the igneous rock and adjacent sediments

❏ effects of subsequent deformation and metamorphism

❏ representative examples of different ages of igneous activity.

Cornubian granite batholith network

This network illustrates the variations within the Cornubian batholith which outcrops in a series of distinct masses such as Dartmoor, Bodmin Moor and Land's End (Figure 51). However, these masses are connected deep within the crust into a large east–west-trending granite batholith. The network encompasses the following geological situations:

❏ variations in the mineral composition and texture of different parts of the individual granite masses reflecting differences in the original magma composition, age, crystallisation history, mode of intrusion and late-stage changes

❏ relationships between the granite and the country rocks, including normal contacts, roof pendants (country rock which roofs the batholith) and xenoliths (fragments of country rock contained within the batholith)

❏ the nature of late-stage processes associated with hydrothermal activity, such as the development of china clay, greisen (granitic rock affected by the action of chemically rich vapours) and mineral veins (the metallogenesis associated with these granites will be covered in a separate Geological Conservation Review volume) and

❏ the occurrence of minor intrusions, such as

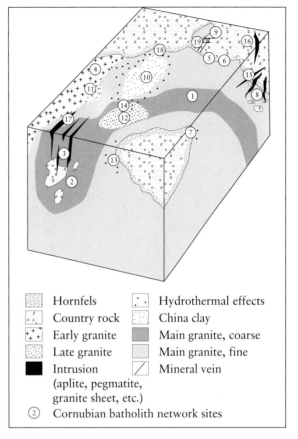

Hornfels   Hydrothermal effects
Country rock   China clay
Early granite   Main granite, coarse
Late granite   Main granite, fine
Intrusion   Mineral vein
(aplite, pegmatite,
granite sheet, etc.)
②   Cornubian batholith network sites

Figure 52. *Schematic diagram of the Cornubian granite batholith. The numbers refer to the sites described in the table on page 60.*

granite cupolas (dome-like protuberances from the main body of the batholith), and aplites (a sugary-textured igneous rock) and pegmatites (a coarsely crystalline igneous rock with crystals three or more centimetres long).

The sites selected for this network are tabulated on page 60.

The network is further illustrated by Figure 52 which places each of the sites on a generic granite batholith diagram. The figure demonstrates how relatively few sites have been identified to characterise one of the major granitic bodies in Britain for the Geological Conservation Review.

Post-orogenic volcanic network

This network illustrates the different types of lava which erupted into the desert environment that existed after the close of the Variscan Orogeny, in late Carboniferous and Permian times, when the granite masses formed high ground that was undergoing active erosion.

IGNEOUS ROCKS OF SOUTH-WEST ENGLAND BLOCK: CORNUBIAN GRANITE BATHOLITH NETWORK

SITE NAME	*GCR SELECTION CRITERIA*
1 Haytor Rocks Area	Representative of the coarsely-crystalline Dartmoor Granite.
2 Birch Tor	Representative of a suite of rocks included within the granite (xenoliths).
3 De Lank Quarries	Representative of coarse-grained Bodmin Moor Granite with xenoliths and dykes.
4 Luxulyan Quarry	Representative of coarse granite formed early in the sequence at St Austell. 'Internationally renowned' for *in situ* occurrence of the British rock type luxullianite.
5 Leusdon Common	Representative of the complex relationships between granite intrusion and country rocks.
6 Burrator Quarries	Representative of the contact between the granite and the Devonian sediments. 'Internationally renowned' as a site where the contact of the granite can be seen.
7 Rinsey Cove (Porthcew)	Representative of the upper part of the granite intrusion.
8 Cape Cornwall area	Representative of the contact between the Land's End Granite and the country rock.
9 Porthmeor Cove	Representative of two small satellites of the Land's End Granite.
10 Wheal Martyn	Representative of the granite which provides the source of the china clay.
11 Carn Grey Rock and Quarry	Representative of granite intermediate in type between the two at St Austell.
12 Tregargus Quarry	Representative of variants of the St Austell Granite.
13 St Mewan Beacon	Representative of a rare rock type formed in the rocks roofing the granite.
14 Roche Rock	Representative of a rare rock rich in the mineral tourmaline.
15 Megiliggar Rocks	Representative of a complex contact between the granite and baked country rock.
16 Meldon Aplite Quarries	Representative of a large fine-grained dyke formed at a late stage in the development of the granite. 'Internationally renowned' for its unusual minerals.
17 Praa Sands (Folly Rocks)	Representative of a multiple granitic dyke.
18 Cameron (Beacon) Quarry	Representative of the contact of the St Agnes Granite with its country rock.
19 Cligga Head area	Representative of minerals created in the country rock by a small granite body, and their process of formation.

The network illustrates the following geological situations:

❑ the considerable variations in mineralogy and rock type between different localities, some rock types being relatively unusual

❑ the nature of the relationships between the igneous rock and the adjacent sediments.

Lizard and Start complexes network

These complexes represent the remnant of an ancient sea floor which has been significantly metamorphosed and deformed to the point that interpretation is difficult and can be controversial. The network illustrates the complicated geological history to which these rocks have been subjected, encompassing the following geological situations:

❑ variations in ocean-crust rocks such as basalt, gabbro and peridotite

❑ the presence of gneiss and schist associated with multiple deformation phases

❑ the range of occurrence of igneous bodies such as pillow lavas and dykes

❑ complex contacts between rock types of different age and origin

❑ the influence of metamorphism.

PALAEOZOIC PALAEOBOTANY GEOLOGICAL CONSERVATION REVIEW BLOCK

GEOLOGICAL CONSERVATION REVIEW NETWORKS

● Silurian network
  (worked example given)

● Devonian network

● Lower Carboniferous network

● Upper Carboniferous network

● Permian network.

At the beginning of the Palaeozoic Era, single-cell plants had existed for over 3000 million years but had probably been restricted to aqueous, mainly marine, environments. Plants had evolved in the seas and were adapted to an environment which supported their tissues, bathed them in nutrients, contained dissolved gases for respiration and photosynthesis, and allowed, in those plants which employed sexual reproduction, the male gametes to swim to the ova. For such plants the land was a hostile environment. 'Soils' were sparse and poor in nutrients. Photosynthesis and respiration had to take place in the air where the environment was dry. The air provided no support for above-ground vegetation and, away from damp ground, the male gametes were unable to swim to the ova. But, by the end of the Palaeozoic Era, plants had developed features that would enable them to overcome all these problems.

To succeed on land, plants required (1) water-resistant surface tissues (cuticle) and spores, (2) strengthening mechanisms to support the weight of their aerial tissues, (3) a means of conveying water and nutrients from the soil to the aerial tissues, as well as oxygen and the products of photosynthesis back to the roots, and (4) the means of fertilising ova in dry conditions.

By the end of the Silurian Period, the first vascular plants had developed which combined moisture-resistant surface tissues and spores with the development of strengthening and water-conducting structures within the stems. These developments continued in the Devonian Period with the appearance of secondary wood and an increasing sophistication of the other structures. By the late Devonian, the first seed plants (gymnosperms) appeared, together with tree-like roots. In the Carboniferous, pteridophyte forests (tree ferns and giant club-mosses up to 40 metres high) dominated the equatorial delta areas, and the main classes of seed plants evolved. In 'Europe' and 'North America', the drier conditions of the Permian saw the pteridophyte forests in decline and the proliferation of the seed plants.

These changes took place during the Palaeozoic Era over a period of 200 million years. The Geological Conservation Review treats the topic by selecting sites on the basis of five networks: Silurian, Devonian, Lower Carboniferous, Upper Carboniferous and Permian. Evolutionary networks are an example of networks where there may be gaps in the site record. Plants existed, and may have been fossilised, which show all the stages in the evolutionary development, but some of these have yet to be found. An example of a network in the Palaeozoic Palaeobotany Block is the Silurian network.

Silurian network

This network represents the different types of fossil plant from the Silurian Period (ranging from 445 to 395 million years ago). Britain

PALAEOZOIC PALAEOBOTANY BLOCK: SILURIAN NETWORK

SITE NAME	*GCR SELECTION CRITERIA*
1 Pen-y-Glog Quarry, Clwyd	Representative of early land plants in the Silurian Period, the oldest known in Britain, including examples of *Prototaxites*. Preserves the oldest-known terrestrial plant cell structures in the world.
2 Llangammarch Wells Quarry, Powys	Representative of Silurian marine plants, including the non-calcareous alga *Powysia*.
3 Rockhall Quarry, Hereford and Worcester	Representative of Silurian marine plants, particularly the alga *Inopinatella*.
4 Cwm Craig Ddu Quarry, Powys	Representative of early Silurian land plants, and has yielded the oldest specimens of *Cooksonia* in Britain and one of the oldest records of *Cooksonia* in the world.
5 Capel Horeb Quarry, Powys	Representative of early land plants, including *Nematothallus*, *Cooksonia* and *Steganotheca*. Contains the oldest-known plants with vascular tissue in the world.
6 Perton Lane, Hereford and Worcester	Representative of the earliest land vegetation. Central to any discussion of early land ecosystems. The type locality for *Cooksonia*.
7 Freshwater East, Dyfed	Representative of the diversity of the early land flora. The most diverse land flora of Silurian age in the world, and has yielded the oldest known examples of spiny axes.

has the most complete known record of Silurian land plants in the world. Most of the sites are in Wales and the Welsh Borders. The climate in which these plants grew was tropical and the conditions humid, warm and equable — highly suited to the colonisation of the land by plants.

Marine algae (seaweeds) existed throughout the Palaeozoic Era and vascular plants are believed to have evolved from the green algae group, perhaps from an ancestor shared with the stoneworts, a group characteristic of freshwater habitats. A spectacular early non-vascular terrestrial plant was *Prototaxites* which had thick 'trunks' that lay prostrate on the land surface and were constructed of a mass of tubes which may have functioned like vascular tissue. Another land plant, *Nematothallus*, was probably an encrusting plant, where the tissue was not differentiated into leaves, stems or roots. However, the most significant of the Silurian plants were small with simple stems branching into two, known as rhyniophytoids, including *Cooksonia* and *Steganotheca*. These are generally considered to have included the earliest vascular plants, and examples of slender axes (albeit without the characteristic spore-bearing bodies) with true vascular tissue are reported from the Ludlow Series.

Gas and water exchange was possible through surface cells called stomata, which opened or closed to control this exchange.

The network can be illustrated diagrammatically on the basis of the presence of adaptive structures for life on land. Figure 53 demonstrates this concept, showing where the selected sites fit into the network.

During the succeeding periods of the Palaeozoic, the evolution of features adapted to life on land continued and all the main classes of plants, except the flowering plants appeared. For most of this period the climate continued to be tropical and, in the diverse swamp forest communities, plants competed for space and light, encouraging the development of tall stems and frond-like foliage. Towards the end of the Palaeozoic era, drier conditions favoured adaptations less dependent on moist conditions. The features of the four remaining networks are summarised below.

Devonian network

By the end of the Devonian all the major groups of vascular plants were present except the flowering plants. Important characteristics of the Devonian network are:

Figure 53. *Schematic diagram showing the evolution of structures that are necessary for plants to survive on land. The numbers refer to the sites described in the table on page 62.*

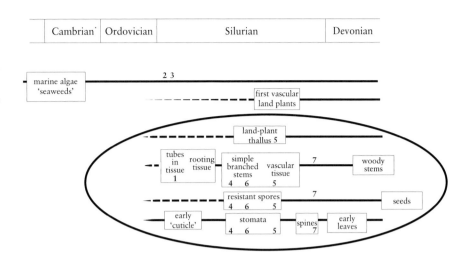

❑ the evolution of plant structures, including laminate foliage, seeds, secondary wood and tree-like forms up to 20 metres high
❑ the development of major plant groups, including clubmosses, horsetails, fern-like plants and seed plants
❑ colonisation of upland areas away from wet basins
❑ ecologically important plant assemblages reflecting various environmental conditions.

Lower Carboniferous network

The Lower Carboniferous saw few really significant structural developments in plants; it was a time of consolidation of the developments that had taken place in the Devonian Period. However, seed plants diversified and a group called pteridosperms, which had fern-like fronds, produced seeds and often grew to tree size. Important characteristics of the Lower Carboniferous network were:

❑ the diversification of early ferns and fern-like plants, clubmosses, horsetails and seed plants
❑ the development of the earliest extensive forest habitats
❑ ecologically important plant assemblages reflecting various environmental conditions.

Upper Carboniferous network

While evolutionary advances took place in the tropical uplands (e.g. the appearance of conifers) and at higher latitudes, the plant fossils of the tropical lowland habitats are of interest primarily because they reflect the high point of forest vegetation dominated by clubmosses up to

40 metres high and, towards the end of the period, by tree-ferns, pteridosperms and cordaites, a conifer-like group. The productivity of these forests is reflected in the fact that this was the main period of deposition or organic material that became coal. Important characteristics of the Upper Carboniferous network are:

❑ the diversification of earlier forms, including ferns and seed plants
❑ the development of adaptations assisting growth in drier areas, including seed plants
❑ diversity of the plant communities of the lowland swamp forests
❑ ecologically important plant assemblages reflecting various environmental conditions.

Permian network

The increasingly arid conditions during the Permian Period in 'Britain' caused the extinction of the Carboniferous swamp-forest vegetation dominated by clubmosses and horsetails, and their replacement by ferns and seed plants, particularly conifers. There are few good Permian sites in Britain that contain plant fossils. The network's important characteristic is to demonstrate the changing nature of forest communities facing conditions of increasing aridity.

QUATERNARY GEOLOGICAL CONSERVATION REVIEW NETWORKS: ENGLISH LOWLAND VALLEY RIVERS

The geological history of the Quaternary Period in the major valleys of southern England is the same as their geomorphological history. The

Table 2. Each row represents a period of time, where stages with odd numbers correspond to interglacials, and even numbers to ice ages.

Geological deposit (or event) Compare with Figure 54	British stage	Oxygen isotope stage	Age in years before present	Lower Thames Quaternary Geological Conservation Review sites (Bridgland, 1994)
Alluvium Shepperton Gravel (river down-cutting — buried channel) East Tilbury Marshes Gravel	Holocene Devensian	1 5d-2	5000	
Interglacial deposits at *Trafalgar Square*	Ipswichian	5e	125,000	
Spring Gardens Gravels (river down-cutting) Mucking Gravel (late)	unnamed	6		
Interglacial deposits at *Aveley*	unnamed	7	215,000	Northfleet (Ebbsfleet Valley): Baker's Hole Complex; Aveley, Sandy Lane Quarry
Mucking Gravel (early) (river down-cutting) Corbets Tey Gravel (late)	unnamed	8		Lion Pit Tramway Cutting
Interglacial deposits at Belhus Park	Hoxnian	9	320,000	Purfleet–Bluelands, Greenlands, Esso and Botany Pits
Corbets Tey Gravel (early) (river down-cutting) Orsett Heath Gravel (late)	unnamed	10		Globe Pit, Little Thurrock
Interglacial beds at *Swanscombe*	Swanscombian	11	400,000	Swanscombe
Orsett Heath Gravel (early) Dartford Heath Gravel Hornchurch Till (glacial deposits)	Anglian	12	about 450,000	Wansunt Pit, Hornchurch Railway Cutting

Ages, in thousands of years at the mid-point of the stage, are given. Note that some gravel deposits (e.g. the Mucking Gravel) accumulated over three stages. Italics show sites where the age has been established by amino-acid dating of protein in fossil shells. This table should be compared with Figure 54.

evidence consists of old river gravels preserved at different elevations in the valleys as river terraces. They increase in age with increasing height above the present floodplains. As such, they form a 'staircase', each step consisting of a gravel terrace, the top of which approximately represents the remains of an ancient floodplain surface. They have been preserved as a series of steps because the rivers have cut vertically downwards in response to climatic change and uplift of the land.

This unique relationship between geological deposit and landform is an invaluable opportunity to explore and understand the geological and geomorphological development of lowland England and the way in which it responded to climatic changes. Its importance is enhanced further because the later stages of terrace development coincided with the earliest human occupation of the British Isles.

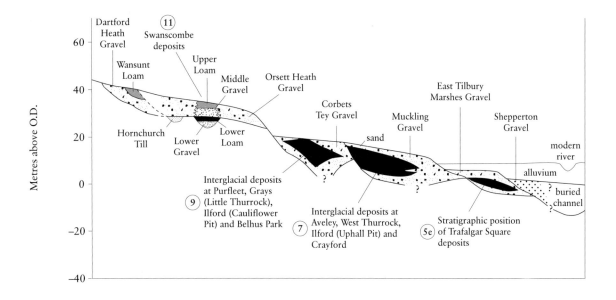

Figure 54. *Diagrammatic section of the Lower Thames Valley. Oxygen isotope stages of interglacial deposits (black) are shown circled. After Bridgland (1994).*

GEOLOGICAL CONSERVATION REVIEW NETWORKS IN THE QUATERNARY OF THE THAMES BLOCK

- The Upper Thames Basin

- The Middle Thames

- The Lower Thames
  (worked example given)

- Essex.

Hand axes fashioned by prehistoric people are often found within the old river gravels. Thus the geological history, landform (geomorphological) history, and prehistory and archaeology are related by the contents of the Quaternary sediments and the landforms they comprise.

The remains of these river gravels which were deposited throughout southern England, for example, in the Thames, Avon and Severn valleys, are the basis for several Geological Conservation Review networks. The older the gravel deposits, the less likely they are to have been preserved, and many site 'gaps' exist in the lowland river valley Quaternary networks because the evidence has been destroyed, by either natural processes or gravel extraction.

The Thames Valley is an example of a river

system that has evolved over nearly two million years. Three principal phases occurred in its development.

1   When the 'Thames' flowed between what is now Reading, Watford, St Albans and Hertford into East Anglia and then the North Sea. Early in this phase its headwaters may have extended into Wales, because igneous rocks from North Wales are contained in its river gravels. These may have been introduced into its headwaters by early Welsh upland glaciers.

2   When a large ice sheet during the Anglian glaciation, some 450,000 years ago, blocked the formerly north-east flowing course of the 'Thames' and it adopted its present path through what is now central London to the Thames Estuary.

3   The development of the Thames since the Anglian glaciation, when extensive river gravels were deposited along its present-day valley: for example, the Taplow Terrace which forms the widespread 'flat' areas around Slough and Heathrow Airport.

These three phases are represented by more than one Geological Conservation Review network, each of which exemplifies stages in the evolution of the Thames Valley. Figure 54 shows a diagrammatic section of the Lower Thames Valley. Twelve distinct stages are represented here, each one corresponds to a major event in the history of the valley that is correlated with a global event as revealed in the oxygen isotope stratigraphy of deep-ocean sediments (Table 2). Oxygen isotope stages 1, 5e, 7, 9 and 11 correspond to interglacials, when global ice-volume was similar to the present. Stages 2, 3, 4, 5, 6, 8, 10 and 12 correspond to ice ages. The ages of the mid-points of the interglacials are shown. These are based on amino-acid dating, which is also the basis for correlating the Lower Thames deposits with those elsewhere in Britain.

The first column in Table 2 shows the named geological deposits and down-cutting events of the river. All of the river gravels were deposited in a periglacial environment, when ice sheets occupied northern Britain. Their braided streams had very wide floodplains.

Figure 54 shows the main geomorphological terrace features of the Lower Thames. Its complicated history may be explored further in Table 2. This complex evolution occurred during five major ice ages and five interglacials (including the present one).

The degree of natural preservation of the Thames deposits varies considerably. The older ones are the most dissected, while those deposited after the Anglian glaciation are relatively better preserved. All of them, however, have been subject to destruction or modification through natural erosion, as well as by quarrying activities for sand and gravel aggregates. They are still an important and valuable economic resource.

THE COASTAL GEOMORPHOLOGY OF SCOTLAND GEOLOGICAL CONSERVATION REVIEW BLOCK

Much of the coastline of Scotland consists of relatively old rock types of variable resistance to erosion, ranging from the ancient, durable Lewisian rocks of the north-west to the younger, less resistant Devonian Old Red Sandstone sediments and Carboniferous lavas of the east. Younger Tertiary lavas, prone to landsliding where underlain by weaker sediments, form the coastline of parts of the Inner Hebrides. The variations in hardness and rock structure (jointing and bedding) have a fundamental control on the overall coastline form and on the shape of the landforms. In addition, rock structures, such as major faults, have played a part in coastline form, most notably in the pattern of sea lochs in western Scotland.

Apart from rock type and structure, factors such as climate, wind, tide and wave action, the effects

GEOLOGICAL CONSERVATION REVIEW NETWORKS

Beach complexes of the Highlands and Islands

● *Beach-machair system*

● *Beach-dune-machair system (worked example given)*

● *Beach-bar system*

● *Prograding coastal foreland*

Beach complexes of lowland Scotland

● *Beach-dune system*

● *Prograding coastal foreland*

● *Shingle structures*

Rock coast geomorphology

● *Cliffs and related features*

● *Shore platforms*

● *Archipelago*

Saltmarsh geomorphology

● *Barrier beach*

● *Estuary*

● *Loch head.*

of glaciation and sea-level change, vegetative 'protection' and the availability of sediment supply all play a role in shaping the coast, the stability of the present coastal environment and the effects of present-day geomorphological processes.

Broadly, the interrelationships between these factors make it possible to classify types of coastline into beach complexes, rock-coast features and saltmarshes. The beach complexes can be categorised further into distinctive types for the Highlands and Islands (beach-machair system, beach-dune-machair system, beach-bar system, prograding coastal foreland) and lowland Scotland (beach-dune system, prograding coastal foreland and shingle structures). Similarly, the rock coast and saltmarsh coastlines can be subdivided further. These categories form the basis of Geological Conservation Review networks.

COASTAL GEOMORPHOLOGY OF SCOTLAND BEACH-DUNE-MACHAIR SYSTEM OF THE HIGHLANDS AND ISLANDS

SITE NAME	GCR SELECTION CRITERIA
Central Sanday, Orkney	Representative assemblage of beach, dune and machair landforms and processes in an area of coastal submergence; includes an assemblage of tombolos, bars and spits.
Traigh na Berie, Western Isles	Representative beach-dune-machair complex notable for its wide range of landforms and processes.
Pabbay, Western Isles	Representative of machair and dune surfaces important for interpreting the development of these features associated with coastal submergence.
Luskentyre and Corran	Representative of a dynamic beach-dune-machair system.
Seilebost, Western Isles	Representative of a beach complex developed in a relatively low-energy environment.
Hornish and Lingay Strand/ Machair Robach and Newton, Western Isles	Representative assemblage of beach-dune-machair features such as machair dissection and coastline recession.
Ardivachar and Stoneybridge, Western Isles	Internationally important and representative of a wide range of beach-dune-machair complexes in a high-energy environment modified by a shallow nearshore zone. Imprtant for showing geomorphological interrelationships between features. Type area for machair landforms and development.
Eoligarry, Western Isles	Representative of landforms and processes of dune and machair erosion.
West coast of Jura, Strathclyde	Internationally important and representative of raised shorelines, but also includes beach, dune and machair features, notably the relatively rare cliff-foot type of machair.
Machir Bay, Strathclyde	Representative beach-dune-machair complex in a high-energy environment. Exceptional for machair ridge and hillside forms and for showing water-table and drainage controls on machair and dune morphology.
Dunnet Bay, Highland	Representative site for showing the scale of dune and machair landforms and modern-day processes.

Beach complexes of Scotland

Beach complexes are widely distributed throughout Scotland. Typically they comprise beaches, sand dunes, machair (dune pasture with lime-rich soils), links or some combination of these. In the north and west, and particularly in the Outer Hebrides and Shetland, they are associated with high-energy, exposed environments; in the south and east, lower levels of energy and exposure prevail. Modern active shingle structures are relatively rare, although there are extensive sites of raised shingle ridges in many areas. In a British context, the beach complexes of Scotland are nationally important for:

- ❏ the machairs of the Highlands and Islands which are exceptionally rare in western Europe (some examples occur in north-west Ireland)
- ❏ features associated with high-energy, exposed environments
- ❏ some of the largest British blown-sand features
- ❏ some of the most extensive areas of sand coast progradation
- ❏ features associated with glaciated coasts.

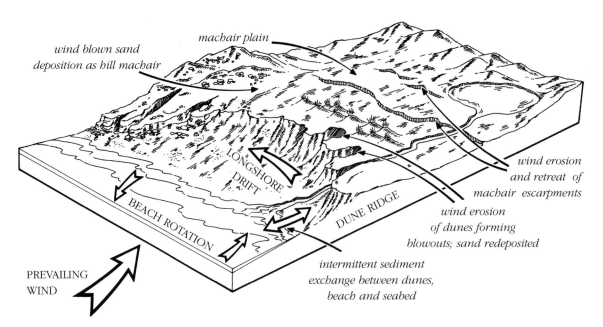

wind blown sand
deposition as hill machair

machair plain

LONGSHORE DRIFT

BEACH ROTATION

DUNE RIDGE

PREVAILING WIND

intermittent sediment
exchange between dunes,
beach and seabed

wind erosion
and retreat of
machair escarpments

wind erosion
of dunes forming
blowouts; sand redeposited

Figure 55. *The beach-dune-machair network addresses the variations in landforms and processes which occur in the Highlands and Islands area affecting this type of beach complex. The network covers the range and diversity of active and relict geomorphological features. Drawing by C. Ellery.*

Beaches of the Highlands and Islands networks

Sandy beaches comprise less than 5% of the total length of the coastline of the Highlands and Islands. Most of the beaches occur on the islands on the open, highly exposed Atlantic coasts, and to a lesser extent in north and east Sutherland. This distribution is related to four principal controlling factors: exposure, relief of the coastal zone, rock type and glacial history. Many beaches in the region are associated on the landward side with blown-sand deposits in the form of sand dunes or machair, forming what are called beach complexes. Glaciation has been an important factor in beach-complex development: first, in providing a source of sediments, and second, in influencing changes in sea level over time and space, which have left a strong imprint.

The beach-complex network illustrated here is the beach-dune-machair system of the Highlands and Islands.

Beach-dune-machair system

The beach complexes associated with machair development are among the most distinctive soft coast systems of Britain. The Geological Conservation Review network which addresses this system includes all the associated major features (landforms and processes) and encompasses their history of development and their variations according to the principal controlling factors. This network is shown diagrammatically in Figure 55.

Twelve sites were selected for this network to illustrate the features of the beach-dune-machair system, with preference being given to those sites that show outstanding examples of landforms or landform assemblages in the beach-dune machair system and sites that offer opportunities to elucidate the links between landforms and the processes which form them as well as the history of their development. Emphasis was placed on selecting sites with assemblages of features. The importance of each site is summarised in the table on page 67.

Beach and dune coasts of lowland Scotland networks

Sandy beaches form a relatively large part of the coastline of lowland Scotland, notably on the east coast. This reflects the less indented nature of the coastline in comparison with that of the Highlands and Islands, and the reworking of large volumes of sediment which had been deposited on the continental shelf during deglaciation. Larger beaches are typically long and curved with a single dune line, and extensive links are developed on older low raised beaches. The beach and dune coasts of lowland Scotland can be grouped into three models:

- beach-dune systems with parallel dune ridges, illustrating the development of different dune types and blown-sand deposits
- prograding foreland systems, showing the scale, complexity and diversity of the landforms and processes associated with coastal progradation, such as stabilised dune sands and dynamic spit and bar environments
- shingle structures showing the assemblage of active and raised shingle ridges and shingle spits.

Rock coast geomorphology networks

Rock coast features are characteristic of extensive parts of western Scotland from the Clyde Estuary to Shetland and including the north coast of the mainland. They include large glaciated sea lochs, low ice-scoured coasts, low cliffs with shore platforms of variable width and extent, and high cliffs, varying according to patterns of rock type, glacial erosion and isostatic uplift. To the east and south-west, rock coasts are more intermittent or buried in drift or sand overlying shore platforms. The rock coast features of Scotland are important for

- features associated with igneous and metamorphic rocks
- features associated with high-energy exposed environments
- some exceptionally high-cliff coast features
- features associated with glaciated coasts.

Saltmarsh geomorphology networks

Saltmarshes are limited in distribution in Scotland and are confined to a number of estuary, barrier-beach and loch-head settings. They are important for:

- features associated with crustal uplift
- relatively young features that allow comparisons to be made with more developed systems in England
- features associated with loch-head environments.

THE GEOLOGICAL CONSERVATION REVIEW SITE SERIES

The examples described above show something of how the network approach deals with the range of situations and circumstances that British geology and geomorphology encompass, and the flexibility of the approach in developing a comprehensive series of representative sites that illustrate the characteristics of each block.

The suite of Geological Conservation Review sites is derived from the selection of the international, exceptional and representative sites discussed above. Of course, the great majority of the internationally important and exceptional sites were also selected as representative sites because they were the best example for portraying an essential characteristic within a relevant block.

The Geological Conservation Review site series is summarised in Figure 56. The figure lists the Geological Conservation Review blocks and indicates how these blocks will be grouped for publishing within the Geological Conservation Review volume series. The numbers and distribution of sites across Great Britain within these volumes are also shown.

The selection of individual sites to represent the essential characteristics of the blocks was a major element of the work of the Geological Conservation Review. The methods employed to do this are described in the next chapter.

Figure 56. *List of blocks.*

GCR volume	GCR blocks	Distribution of sites		
		England	Scotland	Wales
STRATIGRAPHY				
Tertiary	Paleogene Neogene	45		
Upper Cretaceous	Cenomanian–Maastrichtian	35	2	
Marine Lower Cretaceous	Berriasian–Barremian Aptian–Albian	45		
Jurassic–Cretaceous Boundary Interval	Portlandian–Berriasian Wealden	72		

		Distribution of sites		
GCR volume	**GCR blocks**	**England**	**Scotland**	**Wales**
Upper Jurassic: Oxfordian–Kimmeridgian	Oxfordian Kimmeridgian	39	5	
Middle Jurassic	Bathonian Callovian Aalenian–Bajocian	101	13	
Lower Jurassic Toarcian	Hettangian, Sinemurian, Pleinsbachian	34	9	2
Permian–Triassic	Rhaetian Permian–Triassic (red beds)	47	10	6
Marine Permian of England	Marine Permian	27		
Upper Carboniferous	Westphalian Namurian (part)	82	9	21
Lower Carboniferous	Dinantian of Scotland Dinantian of northern England and North Wales Dinantian of Devon and Cornwall Dinantian of southern England and South Wales Namurian (part)	89	33	27
Devonian	Non-marine Devonian Marine Devonian	62	22	11
Silurian	Ludlow Wenlock Llandovery	63	14	36
Cambrian–Ordovician	Caradoc–Ashgill Llandeilo Arenig–Llanvirn Arenig–Tremadoc and Cambrian–Tremadoc Tremadoc Cambrian	35	18	71
Precambrian of England and Wales	Precambrian of England and Wales[+] Precambrian Palaeontology	21		13
STRUCTURAL AND METAMORPHIC GEOLOGY				
Moine, Torridonian and Lewisian	Moine[+] Torridonian[+] Lewisian[+]		111	
Dalradian	Dalradian[+]		73	
Variscan to Alpine Structures	Variscan Structures of South Wales and the Mendips Variscan Structures of south-west England Alpine Structures of southern England	42		14

GCR volume	GCR blocks	Distribution of sites		
		England	Scotland	Wales
Caledonian Structures of Great Britain	Caledonian Structures of the Lake District	12	9	20
	Caledonian Structures of the Southern Uplands			
	Caledonian Structures of Wales			
IGNEOUS PETROLOGY				
Caledonian Igneous	Caledonian Igneous	23	81	26
	Old Red Sandstone Igneous			
	Ordovician Igneous			
Igneous Rocks of South-west England	South-west England Igneous	54		
British Tertiary Volcanic Province	Tertiary Igneous	2	50	
Carboniferous–Permian Igneous	Carboniferous–Permian Igneous	17	31	1
MINERALOGY				
1. Metallogenesis	Mineralogy of the Lake District	105	47	22
2. Mineralogy	Mineralogy of the Pennines			
	Mineralogy of the Mendips			
	Mineralogy of the Peak District/ Leicestershire/ Cheshire/ Shropshire			
	Mineralogy of south-west England			
	Mineralogy of Wales			
	Mineralogy of Scotland			
PALAEONTOLOGY				
Fossil Reptiles of Great Britain	Tertiary Reptilia	43	6	1
	Jurassic–Cretaceous Reptilia			
	Permian–Triassic Reptilia			
Fossil Mammals and Birds	Tertiary Mammalia	55	3	10
	Mesozoic Mammalia			
	Pleistocene Vertebrata			
	Aves			
Fossil Arthropods	Palaeoentomology	23	11	
	Arthropoda (excluding insects and trilobites)			
Fossil Fish	Silurian–Devonian Chordata	42	40	3
	Permian/Carboniferous Fish/Amphibia			
	Mesozoic–Tertiary Fish/Amphibia			
Mesozoic Tertiary Palaeobotany	Tertiary Palaeobotany	46	5	1
	Mesozoic Palaeobotany			
Palaeozoic Palaeobotany of Great Britain	Palaeozoic Palaeobotany	12	19	11

GCR volume	GCR blocks	Distribution of sites		
		England	Scotland	Wales
QUATERNARY GEOLOGY AND GEOMORPHOLOGY				
Quaternary of East Anglia and the Midlands	Quaternary of East Anglia Quaternary of the Midlands and Avon Quaternary of eastern England (part: south)	90		
Quaternary of Northern England	Quaternary of north-east England Quaternary of Cumbria Quaternary of eastern England (part: north) Quaternary of the Pennines	66		
Quaternary of South and South-east England	Quaternary of south-east England Quaternary of south central England	44		
Quaternary of South-west England	Quaternary of south-west England Quaternary of Somerset	60		
Quaternary of the Thames	Quaternary of the Thames	46		
Quaternary of Scotland	Quaternary of Scotland		136	
Quaternary of Wales	Quaternary of Wales Tufa* Holocene Sea Levels* Pollen Stratigraphy of England*			72
GEOMORPHOLOGY				
Karst and Caves of Great Britain	Caves Karst	72	3	14
Coastal Geomorphology of Great Britain	Coastal Geomorphology of Scotland Coastal Geomorphology of Wales Coastal Geomorphology of England Saltmarsh Morphology	45	41	13
Fluvial Geomorphology of Great Britain	Fluvial Geomorphology of Scotland Fluvial Geomorphology of England Fluvial Geomorphology of Wales	35	27	19
Mass Movement	Mass Movement	18	6	3

* Sites will be included in the relevant regional Quaternary volume.
\+ Includes all metamorphic, tectonic, igneous and stratigraphic features of interest.

Chapter 5

Practical Geological Conservation Review selection methods

Figure 57. *Kildrummie Kames esker system, Inverness District, viewed towards the east. Two areas of braided ridges (right foreground and centre distance) are linked by a single ridge. These striking features were produced by glacial meltwater rivers at the end of the last ice age. Photo: Cambridge University Collection. Reproduced by permission of the Curator of Aerial Photography.*

SITE SELECTION CRITERIA

The three essential components of the Geological Conservation Review are explained in Chapter 4. Practical guidelines were also developed so that Geological Conservation Review sites can be selected from the range of candidate sites.

First, two operational criteria are employed.

❏ there should be a *minimum of duplication* of interest between sites
❏ it should be *possible to conserve* any proposed site in a practical sense.

All scientific factors being equal, sites that cannot be conserved, or which entirely or largely duplicate the interest of another, are excluded. Sites that are least vulnerable to potential threat, are more accessible and are not duplicated by other sites are preferred.

Preference is given to sites that:

❏ demonstrate an assemblage of geological features or scientific interests

❏ show an extended, or relatively complete, record of the feature of interest. In the case of geomorphological sites, this often equates to sites that contain features which have been least altered after formation (e.g. Kildrummie Kames, Inverness District; Figure 57). For Quaternary networks, this might relate to sites containing an extended fossil record, including pollen, insects and molluscs. This can be used to infer vegetation history or environmental change
❏ have been studied in detail and which have a long history of research and re-interpretation;
❏ have potential for future study
❏ have played a significant part in the development of the Earth sciences, including former reference sites, sites where particular British geological phenomena were first recognised, and sites which were the focus of studies that led to the development of new theories or concepts.

Application of these criteria ensures that sites chosen for a particular network in the Geological Conservation Review have the greatest collective scientific value and can be conserved.

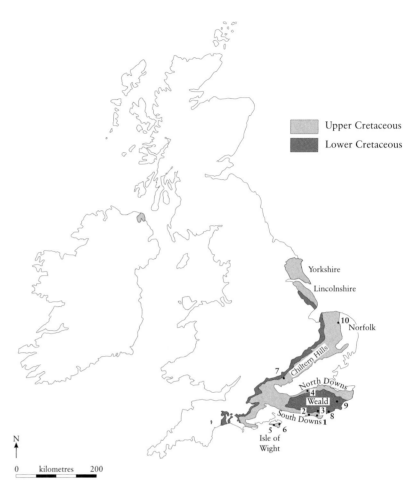

Figure 58. *Ten sites were selected for the fossil reptiles Cretaceous network in Britain to illustrate the range and diversity of reptiles of this period. Some 150 sites were considered as potential sites for this network. The sites not included as SSSIs may be conserved by other means, such as RIGS or local nature reserves.*

Minimum number and minimum area of sites

In order to ensure that Geological Conservation Review site status is confined to sites of national importance, the number of sites selected is restricted to a reasonable minimum. Only those that are necessary to characterise the network in question, that is to demonstrate the current understanding of the range of Earth science features in Britain for the network, are selected. These factors are important in the justification of the scientific value of a Geological Conservation Review site if it is to be subsequently designated a Site of Special Scientific Interest. For example, the scientific case for conserving a given site is stronger if it is the only one of its kind, or if it is demonstrably the best of a set of similar examples (Figure 58).

The area of a Geological Conservation Review site is always kept to a minimum. For example, in tracing the form of a major structure over a distance of several kilometres, a small number of dispersed, representative 'sample' sites might be

selected — the minimum number and size required to describe and interpret the feature adequately. There are, however, exceptions to this general rule: for example, large sites will be required to represent the range of large-scale glacial landforms in the uplands of Wales or Scotland. In contrast, mine spoil heaps, typically of limited size, normally form relatively small sites.

METHODS AND WORKING PRACTICE

Site selection procedures within the Geological Conservation Review

The process of site assessment and selection for the Geological Conservation Review was led by Nature Conservancy Council staff supported by several hundred Earth scientists contracted to assess sites within their particular area of expertise.

The starting point for this process was to devise a comprehensive classification of blocks (*see* Figure 56) to subdivide the geology and geomorphology of Britain into a series of subject areas. Work on particular blocks typically followed four stages.

Stage 1: Building and briefing the block team

For the larger blocks, a *co-ordinator* (a specialist member of the Nature Conservancy Council or an external expert Earth scientist) was appointed to oversee the task of assessing and selecting the sites. The co-ordinator's role was to advise on site selection criteria and collate the work of a number of contributors who dealt with networks of sites within the block. For the smaller blocks, a single Geological Conservation Review *contributor* often undertook the work, in consultation with other experts within the field.

Stage 2: Literature review and site shortlisting

The block co-ordinator or contributor then undertook an extensive literature search of both published and unpublished sources to create a list of all known Earth science sites of potentially national or international importance, relevant to the subject of the block. Where appropriate, early historical references to specific sites were researched so that potential sites from the earliest days of British Earth science could be considered for inclusion in the review.

Each of the sites on the draft list was given standard basic documentation (e.g. site location, brief summary of scientific interest, possible justification for inclusion within a network).

Draft lists were circulated among the appropriate experts for critical assessment and comment. Sites with significant research potential were considered. Following this peer review, a shortlist of candidate sites was drawn up. In the case of the Jurassic–Cretaceous Reptilia Block, 380 potential Geological Conservation Review sites were identified from the literature as potentially special; this number was reduced to about 150 after first-stage sifting.

Stage 3: Field visits and detailed site investigation

Shortlisted sites were usually visited by the block co-ordinator or relevant expert to assess and validate the scientific interest.

Following the initial field visits, the list of potential sites was refined further by the co-ordinator, in liaison with the specialist advisers for the block. At this stage, sites where significant deterioration of the features of interest had taken place were usually dropped from the list. In some cases it proved necessary to clear exposures of vegetation and soil, or to sample them remotely, for example by augering, before an assessment of potential could be made. This was particularly true of some historically important Quaternary localities.

Stage 4: Final assessment and preparation of Geological Conservation Review site documents

The draft list of potential sites was then reviewed and the sites were once again scrutinised against the selection and operational criteria. A final list of sites meriting inclusion within the particular Geological Conservation Review block was then prepared. From the list of 150 shortlisted potential Jurassic–Cretaceous Reptilia sites, a final list of 28 actual Geological Conservation Review sites was produced.

For each proposed Geological Conservation Review site the following documents were prepared:

❏ a site boundary enclosing the important features of the site, drawn on 1:10,000 Ordnance Survey maps
❏ a concise statement of the scientific interest, typically between 100 and 200 words in length, an example of which is given in Figure 59
❏ a longer statement describing the scientific importance of the site and citing key references from the literature.

The statement and map form the basis of a key part of the documentation required to notify the Geological Conservation Review sites as components of the SSSI system under the *Wildlife and Countryside Act 1981*. The process of work stages applied in selecting sites for a Geological Conservation Review block is shown schematically in Figure 60. SSSIs may contain more than one Geological Conservation Review site; an example is Durlston Bay, South Dorset, SSSI which contains six Geological Conservation Review sites (see information box on page 79).

GCR BLOCK   **Quaternary of Wales**

NAME OF SITE   **Dinas Dinlle**

COUNTY/DISTRICT   **Gwynedd**

GRID REFERENCE   **SH 437562**

GCR INTEREST

Dinas Dinlle is an important coastal exposure for interpreting late Pleistocene glaciation in North Wales. The sequence comprises a complex series of Irish Sea and Welsh tills with associated sands, silts and gravels. It is complicated by well-developed glaciotectonic structures including folds, faults and overthrows, and by cryoturbation features which occur in the uppermost horizons. The sections have been regarded as showing the northernmost occurrence of Irish Sea till belonging to the oldest-known glacial episode in the area (the Trevor Advance), while the glaciotectonic structures have been interpreted as evidence for a later readvance of ice. However, recent research suggests that the sediments and glaciotectonic structures need not be the product of different glacial advances, but can be adequately explained as a multiple drift sequence formed during one glaciation. The drift sequence, and particularly the glaciotectonic structures, make Dinas Dinlle a site of significant interest for reconstructing late Pleistocene processes and events in North Wales.

Figure 59. Specimen citation.

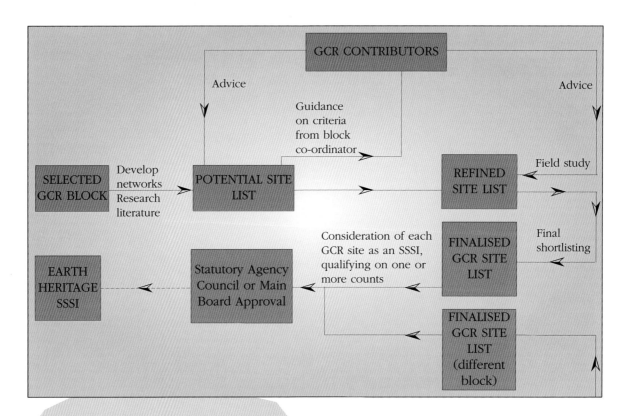

Figure 60. Flow diagram showing a typical site selection process within a GCR block.

Geological Conservation Review sites within Sites of Special Scientific Interest

The 3002 Geological Conservation Review sites identified will be considered for notification as approximately 2300 SSSIs. The difference in numbers reflects the fact that Geological Conservation Review sites chosen as parts of different blocks may partly or entirely overlap geographically. A single SSSI may encompass several Geological Conservation Review sites, as well as one or more features of special biological value. The diagram below shows GCR site overlaps within a single hypothetical SSSI.

Durlston Bay SSSI, South Dorset, is a good example of a large composite site which incorporates separate and overlapping Geological Conservation Review sites.

Photo: J.G. Larwood.

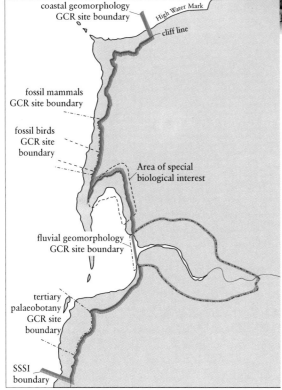

Special features of interest found at Durlston Bay have led to the sites' inclusion in six Geological Conservation Review blocks, as follows:

- ❏ Portlandian–Berriasian Stratigraphy
- ❏ Mesozoic Mammalia
- ❏ Palaeoentomology
- ❏ Mesozoic–Tertiary Fish/Amphibia
- ❏ Jurassic–Cretaceous Reptilia
- ❏ Coastal Geomorphology of England.

Each of the six Geological Conservation Review sites within the single Durlston Bay SSSI was assessed independently for inclusion within its respective network, and judged worthy of Geological Conservation Review status in its own right.

Figure 61. *Florence Mine, Cumbria. Mineralogy of the Lake District Block. The importance of this site lies in its excellent exposures within the Beckerment iron ore body, the largest remaining of the iron ore 'flats' (an ore body that has replaced a sediment layer) of the West Cumbria mining province, and its contribution to research into ore mineralistaion in Britain. At the mine, the variety and form of the ore is displayed* in situ. *This site is one of seven chosen to represent the variety of iron ore deposits across Britain. It is the only one which shows iron ore replacement flats, a type of deposit unrecorded outside Britain. This site was recently added to the Geological Conservation Review.*

At the time of selection of Lake District mineralogy sites, no good in situ *exposures were available at the surface, and a nearby mine dump site was the only available source of material for studying these unique deposits. Florence Mine now supersedes the mine dump site. The photograph shows the mine-roof of kidney ore. This part of the mine is to be conserved with the intention of using it as an educational/visitor resource, consequently no removal of* in situ *specimens is permitted by the mine management. Photo: T. Moat.*

The study of the Earth — continuing developments

The final concept to be considered is 'current understanding'. It is unlikely that the entire geological and geomorphological record will ever be fully understood. Given the speed of scientific change within geology, there is a continual need to re-survey to ensure that the Geological Conservation Review networks and sites reflect the current state of knowledge. The Geological Conservation Review is, therefore, an ongoing process of refinement and update to ensure that conservation keeps pace with current understanding.

The physical character of sites is constantly being changed by weathering and vegetation growth. Some sites are lost to development, while other new exposures are created by quarrying and engineering works (Figure 61). Thus a site series is inherently dynamic and should be reviewed periodically. In practice, such reviews have resulted in only modest changes since 1990.

Chapter 6

Earth heritage conservation

Figure 62. *Coastal defences at Corton Cliff, Suffolk. This site is important as the type section for the Anglian Stage (part of the Quaternary Period), during which the most extensive glaciation of Britain occurred. **(a)** The coastal section as it appeared in 1964, before modern sea defence works were undertaken. To the right lies the old sea wall, built in the late nineteenth century to protect a private estate. The wall remained intact until the turn of the twentieth century, indicating the extent of cliff erosion over 60 years.*

(b) *The stabilised and vegetated cliffs at Corton. There are two types of structure forming the defence of the cliffs at this locality: a steel and concrete wall and a timber wave screen. Coastal protection works such as these may be in conflict with geological conservation, because for some sites continued erosion is necessary to renew exposures of rock. There is little geological interest in the vegetated slope without resorting to excavation work. Photos: Landform Slides, Lowestoft.*

The need to take active measures to conserve our Earth heritage is, perhaps, less obvious than for biological sites which we need to conserve to ensure the survival of endangered animals, plants and habitats. Rocks are, after all, hard and durable, and some have existed for many millions of years. Similarly, some mature landscapes have remained almost unchanged for centuries. However, natural resources, such as crushed rock, sand and gravel, are required to meet the demands of modern society and careful planning is required to ensure that any important geological feature is not destroyed in this process.

Threats to the Earth heritage

In modern society, there is an increasing need for waste disposal sites. Quarries, gravel pits, old mines and caves have all been used to fulfil this need and some historically important sites have been lost to science as a result.

Some engineering methods can also pose problems for Earth heritage sites. In protecting coastal cliffs from further erosion, rock exposures of value to science may be covered by engineering works (Figure 62). Such practices can also cut off the sediment supplies which feed and maintain shingle bars, beaches, saltmarshes and mud flats, causing them to become eroded by the action of the sea. Similarly, river engineering works have altered natural fluvial geomorphological features, and commercial and industrial developments have destroyed or covered sites. Even the shape of the land has been changed as features are levelled or exploited to extract materials for the construction industry, and the planting of coniferous trees in upland areas has damaged geomorphological features

However, development and the effective conservation of the Earth heritage are not mutually exclusive if properly co-ordinated.

Quarrying and Earth heritage conservation: threats and benefits

Rock exposures created by quarrying and related activities have played a key role in the interpretation of Britain's geology and have proved vital to the development of the Earth sciences over the last 200 years. Although active quarrying and conservation of the Earth heritage may not appear to be compatible, because quarrying is essentially a destructive process, such extraction has also *revealed* more exposures of rock formations, mineral veins and fossil taxa than would otherwise have been known from natural exposures alone. Therefore, quarrying, and indeed road construction, can be both a threat and a potential benefit to our knowledge of Earth heritage. Co-operation between the extraction industry and conservation interests can strike a mutually beneficial balance.

Of course, even when a site has been selected for Earth heritage conservation, it can still be threatened by, for example, a change in use or natural degradation. Conservation is, therefore, not only a matter of site protection and countering potential threats, but also of active management for the long-term maintenance of the features of special interest.

The remainder of this chapter outlines the history of Earth heritage conservation in Britain, explains the current legal framework for the protection of Earth heritage sites, and considers the strategy adopted for practical Earth heritage site conservation.

THE HISTORY OF EARTH HERITAGE CONSERVATION IN BRITAIN

Earth heritage conservation in Britain dates back to the mid-nineteenth century. An early example of the concern to conserve important sites is the action taken to protect Fossil Grove in Glasgow, where well-displayed stumps from Carboniferous tree-like plants called lycopods were enclosed in 1887. They are still protected by Glasgow City Council (Figure 63).

In 1912 the Society for the Protection of Nature Reserves was formed, and gradually there emerged a more systematic approach for

Figure 63. *Fossil Grove, Glasgow. Stumps of a once flourishing forest of lycopods. This tree-like plant grew in a tropical forest which covered this area of southern Scotland during the Carboniferous Period. The trunks, characterised by diamond-shaped leaf scars, grew up to 30 metres before they branched. Photo: A. Gunning.*

identifying sites that merited conservation. In 1941 the Society convened a conference to consider the place of conservation in post-war Britain. The outcome was the establishment of the Nature Reserves Investigation Committee in 1943. This committee identified no fewer than 390 geological sites in England and Wales. A further 60 geological sites were identified in a subsequent report on Scotland.

This early work prompted the Government to create the Wildlife Conservation Special Committee (England and Wales) to examine ways in which the Government could further support the national nature protection effort. Their report, *Conservation of Nature in England and Wales* (Cmd 7122, 1947), laid the foundation for nature conservation. It recognised a twin approach to nature conservation in which scientific activity developed in parallel with aesthetic and recreational concerns.

In 1949 the Nature Conservancy was created by Royal Charter. The Charter empowered the Nature Conservancy to establish National Nature Reserves for the purposes of nature conservation, including geological and 'physiographical' (geomorphological) conservation.

In the same year, Parliament passed the *National Parks and Access to the Countryside Act 1949* — a milestone in the development of conservation legislation. The Act led to the creation of the National Parks in England and Wales, conferred powers on local authorities to create local nature reserves and required the Nature Conservancy to notify local authorities of the location of Sites of Special Scientific Interest (SSSIs) by reason of their flora, fauna or geological or physiographical features. The prominence of Earth heritage considerations in the thinking of the Committee, and subsequently the Act, owes much to the foresight of Sir Julian Huxley and other members of the Committee. While the Act gave no direct protection to SSSIs, Town and Country Planning legislation provides the means of protecting sites from being destroyed by development.

During the 1950s, '60s and '70s, Earth science staff of the Nature Conservancy (1949–1973) and then the Nature Conservancy Council (1973–1991) contributed to the development of the SSSI and National Nature Reserve (NNR) series. A significant development in wildlife conservation was the Nature Conservation Review (1977) which, between 1966 and 1970, evaluated areas of national biological importance in Britain. The Geological Conservation Review commenced in 1977, to provide a parallel audit of the Earth heritage in Great Britain.

At the same time, much activity by the Nature Conservancy Council was devoted to the local and day-to-day concerns of protecting the sites. This was carried out largely by participating as consultees in the development control process of the Town and Country Planning Acts. Also, during this period, voluntary conservation bodies, notably County Naturalists' Trusts, established some Earth heritage sites as non-statutory reserves, while further sites were acquired by local authorities as Country Parks or statutory local nature reserves.

The next major step forward was the enactment of the *Wildlife and Countryside Act 1981*, which improved arrangements for the effective conservation of SSSIs. An additional Earth heritage aspect of the Act, with important implications for landscape conservation, was the provision for Orders to protect areas of limestone pavement.

The *Environmental Protection Act 1990* and the *Natural Heritage (Scotland) Act 1991* subdivided the Nature Conservancy Council into three country-based organisations — the Countryside Council for Wales, English Nature and Scottish Natural Heritage. This re-organisation reflected the desire to bring nature conservation closer to local people. It also afforded the opportunity for the three organisations to develop independent approaches to the subject. Where common concerns and issues arise, such as in setting common standards of practice, the agencies operate through the Joint Nature Conservation Committee (JNCC). The JNCC also has responsibility for research and advice on nature conservation at both United Kingdom and international levels.

Outside the SSSI network the protection of Earth heritage sites is undertaken for the most part by voluntary and locally based groups, often with support from national Earth science societies and institutions. The work of the Geologists' Association and its regional groups is particularly important, and the Conservation Committee of the Geological Society of London is a forum that brings together organisations and groups concerned with Earth sciences and site conservation. Since 1990, voluntary local groups have been established to notify local authorities of Regionally Important Geological and Geomorphological Sites (RIGS; Figure 64). These RIGS groups have grown rapidly and today exist in all English and Welsh counties. Such groups are also being established in Scotland and Northern Ireland. The work of RIGS groups often involves museums, county wildlife trusts, industry and local authorities, as well as local geologists.

Although RIGS have no statutory status, they can be protected in a most effective way through local initiatives. Local authorities respond positively to protect sites that attract local support and will often accommodate their protection within Local and Structure Plans.

The need to protect Earth heritage sites other than SSSIs reflects a number of factors, particularly the demand for educational sites arising from an increase of interest in the Earth sciences. Other Earth heritage sites, with strong aesthetic rather than scientific appeal, are not specifically protected as SSSIs, but are valuable as a stimulation to raising public awareness and appreciation of geology and geomorphology. If such sites are of local, rather than national, importance, they may be protected

Figure 64. *Coombs Quarry, Buckinghamshire: a RIGS. A collaborative effort by the Buckinghamshire RIGS group with the County Council Countryside Section and local geologists opened up and improved this site. This involved the clearance of the overgrown face, the creation of a new exposure, the provision of walkways and fencing, and the placing of boards with on-site interpretation. The geological interest of the site was first noted in 1860, during mapping by the Geological Survey. The rocks here, the Blisworth Limestone Formation, date from the Middle Jurassic, and are about 160 million years old. The nature of the different rock types and fossils of the rock beds are now accessible to study. Photo: L. Davies.*

appreciation of geology and geomorphology. If such sites are of local, rather than national, importance, they may be protected by RIGS schemes. Many geological sites are also of local interest and importance for their flora, fauna, archaeology, mining history or amenity value, and they too may be protected as RIGS.

The network of RIGS groups helps to ensure that RIGS are accessible and, where appropriate, protected. The RIGS scheme nationwide is of great importance and complements the Geological Conservation Review.

EARTH HERITAGE SITE PROTECTION

The legal framework

The *Environmental Protection Act 1990*, the *Natural Heritage (Scotland) Act 1991* and the *National Parks and Access to the Countryside Act 1949* enable the statutory conservation bodies and local authorities to establish and manage, respectively, national and local nature reserves for the conservation of wildlife and Earth heritage features. Land can be bought or leased for the purpose, or contractual agreements can be reached with the owners and tenants of the land to ensure its protection and proper management. The 1949 Act also enables these bodies to make bylaws to protect the reserves from any type of damage. As a last resort, the statutory conservation bodies and local authorities have a power of compulsory purchase.

Over the years a number of Earth heritage nature reserves have been established, such as Wren's Nest National Nature Reserve near Dudley, in the West Midlands, which was secured as an NNR in 1956 (the first in the United Kingdom for geology; Figure 65). The founding of the reserve is in recognition of the exceptional international importance of the site as a source of Silurian-age fossils. The site has yielded a great variety of fossils in a superb state of preservation, the best of which can be found in museums throughout the world.

However, the 1949 Act recognised that it would be a long time before all important wildlife and Earth heritage sites could be acquired as nature reserves, if ever, and so it also contained a provision for the Nature Conservancy (and its successors) to notify local planning authorities of important areas, not yet managed as nature reserves, as SSSIs. Once a local authority is notified of an SSSI in its area, it is able to protect the site from adverse development under the controls provided by the Town and Country Planning Acts.

Individual planning decisions are guided by the Structure, Unitary and Local Plans relating to the area under consideration. Of particular relevance are mineral and waste disposal Local Plans.

As well as enabling applications detrimental to conservation interests to be turned down, the Planning Acts permit conditional consent to be granted. Such consents allow development to proceed on or near an SSSI with adequate safeguards to avoid damage to the important wildlife or Earth heritage features of the site.

Planning legislation (*Town and Country Planning Act 1990* and the *Town and Country Planning (Scotland) Act 1990*) also enables local authorities to enter into agreements with developers about how their land should be managed when development has taken place. These agreements are often negotiated in parallel with the consideration of planning consent. An agreement could, for example, require the developer and any subsequent owner to provide access to a geological exposure for educational or research purposes. If access had been restricted previously, such an agreement could be very beneficial.

The Planning Acts, and their associated General Development Orders, require local authorities to consult with the statutory nature conservation bodies before consenting to a development proposal affecting an SSSI. Various other statutes place a similar requirement on a range of statutory bodies and public utilities, including the water companies and the National Rivers Authority.

In addition, the *Wildlife and Countryside Act* strengthened the protection afforded to SSSIs considerably. This Act requires the statutory nature conservation bodies to inform all the

Figure 65. *The ripple beds at Wren's Nest National Nature Reserve in Dudley, West Midlands, viewed from the purpose-built observation platform. This visually impressive rock surface provides evidence for the environments of the Silurian Period. Similar ripple marks can be seen today on sandy beaches and river estuaries. Scree, at the base of the slope, continues to yield a wealth of fossils, including trilobites, for which Wren's Nest is particularly renowned. Photo: J. Larwood.*

owners and occupiers of an SSSI about the nature of the features of special interest of the site and of the types of activity that could cause damage to those special features. Before carrying out any of these activities, an owner or occupier must give the appropriate statutory nature conservation agency at least four months' notice. This enables the conservation agency to advise the owner or occupier how, if possible, the operation might be carried out without damaging the special interest. If that is not possible, a contractual agreement to protect the site may be negotiated. The financial provisions of such an agreement are calculated in accordance with national guidelines.

If an owner or occupier is determined to carry out a damaging activity, and this activity does not

Figure 66. Hunstanton
Cliffs and Morfa Harlech.
(a) Cliffs at Hunstanton,
Norfolk, exposing normal
white Chalk overlying Red
Chalk and dark-coloured
sandstones. Debris along
the foot of the cliff indicates
erosion, which ensures that
the rocks in the cliff are
always well .exposed.
Because there is no chance
of erosion completely
removing the rock
sequence (as it extends way
back beyond the cliffs). It is
classed as an exposure site.
Photo: C. D. Prosser.

require planning consent, the Secretary of State
may be asked to make a Nature Conservation
Order which extends the period of notice. Such
an Order also has the effect of making it an
offence for a member of the public to damage the
site.

The 1981 Act also contains a provision enabling
a local authority to make a Limestone Pavement
Order, on either landscape or nature conservation
grounds, to prevent the removal of rock from
limestone pavement areas.

Present legislation is proving to be legally
effective. It is equally important, however, that all
concerned   work closely with owners and
occupiers of important sites to promote effective
conservation management.

EARTH HERITAGE CONSERVATION IN PRACTICE

Conservation strategy

Once an Earth heritage site has been
identified as worthy of special protection
measures, a practical conservation
management strategy needs to be developed and
implemented. This strategy involves elements such
as documenting the importance of the site,
planning and implementing practical conservation
and protection measures, site monitoring and site
enhancement. Although developing site
management strategies was not part of the
Geological Conservation Review, such strategies
are a necessary extension of it.

(b) Coastal sand dunes at Morfa Harlech, Gwynedd.
These landforms would be destroyed by erosion or
commercial extraction of sand. Therefore they need
conserving, by allowing them to evolve naturally, and so
they are an example of an integrity site. Photo: S.
Campbell.

Classification of site types

There are two main types of site:

❏ **Integrity sites** contain finite deposits or
landforms which are irreplaceable if destroyed. A
typical situation is a glacial landform of limited

lateral extent, such as a kame terrace or esker (*see* Figure 35). Other examples include presently active, and previously active, geomorphological sites (e.g. Morfa Harlech, Figure 66b), caves and karst, unique mineral, fossil or geological feature sites, and some stratotypes.

❑ **Exposure sites** provide exposures of a rock which is extensive or also well developed below the ground surface. Exposure sites are numerically the more common type and may include exposures in disused and active quarries, cuttings and pits; exposures in coastal and river cliffs (e.g. Hunstanton cliffs, Figure 66a); foreshore exposures; mines and tunnels; inland outcrops and stream sections.

The broad conservation principles for these types of site are different. 'Integrity' sites are, by definition, finite and irreplaceable. To conserve them a more 'protectionist' approach must be adopted. In contrast, the broad conservation principle for exposure sites depends on the maintenance of an exposure, the precise location of which is not always critical. Quarrying may be welcomed under some circumstances because it creates a fresh exposure and progressively reveals new rock surfaces, enabling a rock body to be analysed in three dimensions. Similarly, marine erosion is often vital in the creation of fresh rock faces at coastal sites, particularly in softer rock formations.

Conservation management of a geo-morphological site depends on whether it is a relict landform or an active process site. Broadly, the requirements for the former will be similar to those for 'integrity' geological sites. The management of dynamic environments is, however, more complex, and requires an understanding of geomorphological sensitivity and the capacity of the system to absorb externally imposed stresses.

The consideration of the nature of the site as an 'integrity' or 'exposure' site helps a fundamental conservation principle to be developed: whether to protect the resource or maintain the exposure. Further general conservation principles can be added by considering the actual type of the site itself — whether it is an active quarry or coastal exposure, for example, where the likely threats, opportunities and problems are different. Finally, site conservation principles will need to take into account the precise location of the feature of special interest within the site. If a feature of interest lies at a cliff base in a quarry, conservation measures should ensure that the foot of the cliff is not obscured, but if the only feature is half-way up the rock face of the quarry, access to it may actually

be improved if sand, shingle or other materials were to be placed at the foot of the rock face.

Using this framework of integrity/exposure site, site type, and the location of the particular feature(s) within a site, it is possible to draw up general conservation principles for different types of site, and provide guidance to conservationists as to the likely threats that may affect them. Building on this, a detailed series of guidelines, the *Handbook of Earth Science Conservation Techniques (1990)*, produced by the NCC (now available from the Countryside Council for Wales, English Nature and Scottish Natural Heritage), describes conservation guidelines for more than 50 site scenarios. However, in order to draw up site-specific conservation plans which detail the measures essential to maintaining and conserving the interest of a site, and to identify the measures that would enhance it, detailed assessments need to be made at the site itself.

Practical conservation planning and implementation will involve the following elements:

1. *Documenting the special interest of a site*
   This may be done by reference to scientific literature, by discussion with experts and by direct observation at the site. For the Geological Conservation Review sites, the Review itself provides the firm foundation for the scientific credentials of a site, and site reports are ultimately documented in Geological Conservation Review volumes. Other documentation schemes are also in operation, such as the National Scheme for Geological Site Documentation, briefly described in *Record of the Rocks*, that RIGS groups use for documenting RIGS sites, and provides a record of the geology at sites which can be used for teaching purposes.

2. *Preparing a site conservation plan*
   Information is required about what activities and processes would impair the interest at the site, how it would deteriorate naturally without intervention, and what action would be desirable, or even essential, to maintain the feature(s) of interest. The general scheme of conservation principles (integrity/exposure, type of site and location of the feature(s) at the site) can provide broad guidance. This will lead naturally to a consideration of what site-specific and practical Earth heritage conservation measures will be needed to

ensure that the features of special interest are not obscured, destroyed or damaged, and also to indicate the recommended frequency of monitoring. The country conservation agencies are developing such plans for all Geological Conservation Review sites.

3. *Safeguarding the site*
   Site management involves:

   ❏ periodic monitoring of the condition of a site so as to anticipate and identify the nature of degradation or damage
   ❏ carrying out essential site safeguard measures, and desirable site enhancement operations, in response to the above, for example, site clearance or re-excavation should a feature become obscured.

In the examples below, potential threats at actual sites are described, and practical solutions to some of the problems that sites may face are indicated.

EARTH HERITAGE CONSERVATION IN PRACTICE — SOME EXAMPLES

Fossil and mineral collecting and conservation

The collecting of fossils and minerals is generally regarded as a benign activity which is an integral part of fieldwork. Many specimens are more valuable to science when removed from the rock than they are *in situ*, provided that they are collected in a responsible manner (*see* below), properly housed, curated and made available for use in a suitable museum. An example is an 'exposure site' such as a cliff face subject to erosion, where new fossils will be exposed continually as the cliff line retreats. In this case, the overall fossil resource can be very large, and it is important to collect and record the fossils before they are lost to the sea.

However, some rare fossil or mineral reserves are highly localised and only have a limited supply, such as an accumulation of fossil bones in a cave. At such 'integrity sites', irresponsible collecting can be very damaging. The conservation of such rare and irreplaceable sites in Britain is becoming increasingly important because they represent a finite, non-renewable resource. In many of these cases, conservation of the site will require that collecting is carefully managed to ensure that the maximum amount of information is gained and the site remains available for appropriate use in the future.

Palaeontological and mineralogical sites differ from many other Earth heritage sites in their management requirements, although they suffer the same potential threats as quarries, cliffs, mines or other outcrops. These threats may involve removal of the resource, or it being obscured by infill, afforestation, slope stabilisation or various types of construction. There is also the need to ensure that potentially irreplaceable material collected for research is properly stored and conserved.

The following guidelines constitute good practice.

❏ Obtain permission before collecting on private land, and respect the owner's wishes.
❏ Wear appropriate clothing and footwear. A helmet is essential if collecting near cliffs or quarry faces, and protective goggles if a chisel or hammer is used. Avoid collecting in dangerous situations. If collecting at the coast, consider tide times prior to the visit. Leave details of the collecting site, and your expected time of return, with a responsible person.
❏ Take only a few representative specimens, and if possible collect only from fallen blocks or loose stones — indiscriminate collecting will diminish the resource for future visitors.
❏ If removing a specimen from a rock face, make a careful note of its exact position in relation to surrounding rock; a photograph provides a useful reference. Label the specimen, giving details of where and when it was collected.
❏ If possible, remove a fossil complete with some of the surrounding rock, and protect it in paper or cloth for safe transport.
❏ Large fossils can be a problem for the individual collectors and could be left for others to see; otherwise seek advice from a local museum. Special equipment and lots of time may be required to excavate large specimens properly.
❏ Mineral collecting from old mines poses special problems — such as effects of stability of the old working or gas build up. Old workings should only be entered with an organised group and experienced leaders. Mine dumps can be visited with permission, however.

A leaflet published by the Geologists' Association is available about general conduct and safety on fieldwork.

The activities of collectors, including commercially oriented collectors, can unearth specimens which may otherwise not have come

Figure 67. *The Shap Granite Quarry, Cumbria, showing regular jointing and the unstable face. This is an example of an exposure site. Photo: J. L. Eyers.*

to light. Collectors should be encouraged to work with specialists and museum curators so that every possible opportunity is taken to systematise their collecting and guarantee that material goes into a suitable repository. Irresponsible collecting may destroy an entire site, but is very difficult to control.

Coastal sites

Conservation of the Barton Geological Conservation Review site

The cliffs around Barton-on-Sea in Hampshire (*see* Figure 9) have been renowned for their Tertiary fossils for many years, and are still visited by many people each year. The site gives its name to a division of the Palaeogene sub-Period, the Bartonian Stage. The site is also nationally important for its Pleistocene Solent River Terrace Gravels.

Fossils are still abundant and are revealed by marine erosion. However, because of this erosion, the site has been under threat from coastal protection schemes on numerous occasions in the past. Previously proposed schemes of rock armouring, slope protection and slope grading, and the cutting of drains into the section, have already damaged parts of the site. Nevertheless, sections of natural cliff do remain, immediately east and west of the Barton frontage, although these could be obscured by the expansion of existing protection schemes.

Such exposure sites, susceptible to cliff fall, are often in conflict with engineering schemes seeking to prevent further erosion. Indeed, there

is often intense local pressure to find engineering solutions to the problem of coastal recession. Coastal schemes commonly involve protective armouring (e.g. concrete sea-walls or rock revetments), which is often accompanied by cliff grading as well as drainage pipes and channels. In the extreme, such schemes can lead to the complete obliteration of the geological interest of the site. Alternative methods of coastal protection, achieving the objectives of reducing the level of marine erosion while limiting the impact of erosion on coastal cliffs of geological importance, have been investigated as part of an 'engineering for conservation' initiative.

In the Hampshire example it will only be through close co-operation between English Nature and the local authority that a mutually agreed action plan can be developed, which will afford protection to this world-famous and internationally important site, while at the same time addressing the problems of coastal erosion of local concern.

Active quarries

Conservation at Shap Granite Quarry

Shap Granite Quarry is a working quarry (Figure 67). The danger of falling blocks from unstable faces is brought about largely by the distinctive jointing pattern of the granite, whereby three sets of joints intersect to produce rectangular blocks, many of which are cut and used for decorative building stone. The rest of the granite is crushed and used for aggregates and pipe manufacture.

The quarrying company allows a limited

Figure 68. *Close up of a display block in the 'safe' area of Shap Granite Quarry. One of the main features of the granite is the large crystals of pink feldspar. These may have either developed at an early stage during magma cooling and solidification, or grown later in the solidified granite, during metamorphism. The nature of the dark fragments in the granite is also debated. Some believe that these are actually fragments of a darker magma which was present at great depth, and was intermixed with the paler granite by convection processes, engulfing some of the pink crystals* en route. *Others believe that the dark fragments were part of the surrounding rock which became engulfed and the pink crystals grew within them during metamorphism. Photo: J. L. Eyers.*

number of parties to visit the quarry each year and these are usually directed to an area of prepared display blocks (Figure 68). The quarry face can be seen easily from the display area, but close access is not permitted. The blocks have been carefully selected to show all the features of the granite and its mineralisation and guarantee a selection of the characteristic 'pink' and 'dark' varieties of Shap Granite, unusually zoned minerals, a variety of veins and surface mineralisation. Weathered blocks, illustrating granite decomposition, as well as some specimens from the nearby Blue Quarry, are also on display.

The blocks provide an excellent selection of rocks and minerals which may otherwise not be available on any one visit to the quarry, because working quarries can uncover and then lose interesting features very rapidly. Thus the display represents an excellent way of maintaining the geological and educational interest of the site, while ensuring safety to the public.

Alternatively, agreements can be made with a quarry owner that one exposure face should be available for study as rock extraction progresses, and that a final face should be left intact when quarrying ceases. The precise location of the exposure is not critical in cases where the special interest lies in the rock type which is present throughout a quarry. By 'smooth blasting' the face, rather than production blasting (which is used for normal extraction and tends to leave remaining rock faces shattered), it is possible to

create a stable and safe exposure of the rock for study. When extraction in the quarry is to cease, it is expected that a 'final' exposure will be agreed with the quarry owner and that this would be maintained as a permanent location of interest. This would be subject to the disused quarry considerations outlined below.

Disused quarries

Conservation at Ercall Quarry, Shropshire

The large area of hillside outcrop at Ercall is fairly safe from many of the common threats such as dumping, building construction and afforestation. The site includes a disused quarry (Figure 69), an exposure site. As a result of the cessation of quarrying activity, operations that were considered to constitute 'normal working practice' for mineral extraction are now considered damaging to the SSSI. For instance, activities such as the construction or removal of roads, tracks, walls or ditches, the laying or removal of cables or pipelines above or below ground, and the building of temporary or permanent structures were not considered a threat to the site during the period of active working. However, after active mineral extraction has finished, these operations are possible threats to the remaining exposure.

Disused quarries

Figure 69. *The disused Ercall Quarry in Shropshire displays the Vendian (end 'Precambrian') – Cambrian boundary. The steeply dipping beds are of Cambrian age. These beds contrast distinctly with the pale, non-bedded form of the Precambrian quartzite on the far left of the photograph. Photo: C. D. Prosser.*

Figure 70. *The rock exposure at the disused Kirtlington Quarry in Oxfordshire is important for Middle Jurassic fish fossils. Photo: J. G. Larwood.*

General considerations at disused quarries

At Kirtlington, Oxfordshire (Figure 70), the removal of slumped material that may obscure the lower rock layers may be desirable. Some of the material may, however, be a useful platform for access to higher sections, and it may also provide a resource for sample collecting. In softer sediments, where rock debris may accumulate at the quarry cliff foot, thus obscuring substantial parts of the exposure, it may be advantageous to create a 'stepped' face (*see* Figure 71).

Should a face like this become vegetated, it may be necessary to clean it every few years, although other conservation interests will need to be balanced. For example, a vegetated face may become a valuable nature conservation resource for other reasons, such as butterflies in abandoned chalk quarries.

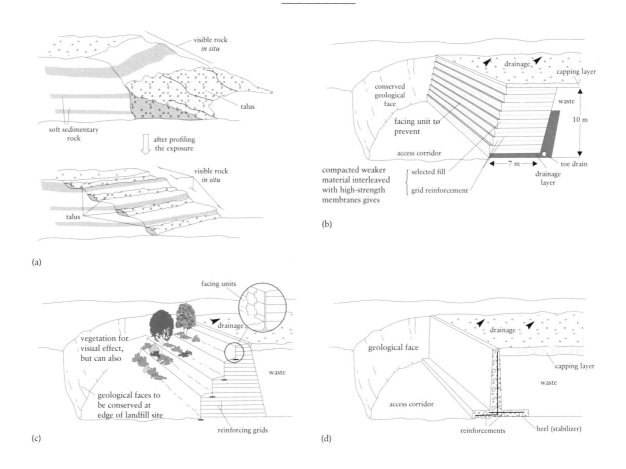

Figure 71. (a) *Diagram of a 'stepped' face in soft sediments which prevents the build up of all of the talus at the cliff foot. Diagrams* **(b)** *to* **(d)** *show idealised sections of conservation schemes within landfill sites.*

Other considerations at sites similar to this could include diverting water run-off away from the rock face of interest, or adding a drainage system nearby to prevent flooding at the base of the face which would impede access. Such exposures may also need to be stabilised, by removing loose rock from a selected area (perhaps by pneumatic breaker or smooth blasting) or by adding supportive mesh or rock bolts to higher sections (if impairing access is not a problem). Any remaining dangerous areas could then be fenced off.

There may also be problems related to fly tipping in disused quarries, and vehicular access to the quarry edge may need to be impeded, perhaps by placing boulders to make a barrier.

Disused quarries as landfill sites

The main threat at the end of the working life of any quarry is subsequent use as a landfill site. However, despite the impacts of landfill, a sympathetically designed scheme incorporating geological exposures can provide an opportunity for the long-term conservation of important faces. M. J. Carter Associates provided an assessment report for the Nature Conservancy Council on the stability of refuse slopes. From this work a number of options have been identified for conservation *within* landfill sites (Figure 71). For example:

❑   contouring the landfill material *around* geological faces

❑   creating reinforced earth walls *around* a geological face

❑   making *alternative exposures* by digging a face outside the proposed landfill site.

Stability, drainage, leachate and landfill gas are the main considerations and cost will play a large part in the choice of the preferred option.

Figure 72. *The spectacular, irreplaceable cave formations of the White River Series, Peak Cavern, Derbyshire.*
Photo: P. R. Deakin.

Cave conservation

Caves (and associated karst sites) can be regarded as 'integrity' sites, because the features of interest are often irreplaceable (Figure 72). The broad conservation approach is therefore based on protection. The inaccessibility of some of these caves protects them to some extent. However, some very good localities have been lost or damaged because of caving activities, quarrying or collection by amateurs or professional dealers. Other activities can also be highly damaging if unmodified, such as effluent disposal and dumping, and entrance closure. Damage from changes in agricultural practice, water abstraction from boreholes and recreational caving can usually be avoided if the activity is sensitively planned and carried out. The use of specific cave conservation plans is one method of addressing the threats to cave sites.

As well as their importance for geology and geomorphology, caves are also important for their archaeology and fauna and flora; for example, they provide important hibernacula and breeding sites for several species of bat. In developing conservation plans for caves, the requirements of each type of interest will need to be balanced.

Issues of safety will be of the utmost importance for geologists studying cave sites, and the National Caving Association (NCA) code of conduct should be followed in this regard. The NCA has also published a National Cave Conservation policy (1995) in association with the statutory conservation agencies, and it describes in detail the issues concerning the conservation of caves.

Figure 73. *Claverley Road Cutting, Shropshire. The site is important for the study of ancient river environments that existed in the Triassic Period. Photo: English Nature.*

Figure 74. *Excavation of dinosaur remains at Brighstone Bay, Isle of Wight. The skeleton seems to be that of a sauropod dinosaur which died on a land surface that was subsequently inundated by flooding. The seemingly chaotic disarticulation and distribution of the bones could be explained by scavenging of the carcass prior to flooding. Photo: S. Hutt.*

Road construction

Conservation of Claverley Road Cutting

In the process of road construction, geological features may be threatened if, for example, a cutting is to be made. On the other hand, this process may also *create* an exposure where there was none before. The conservation principles and practice here will depend on the net effect of creation against removal. The Claverley Road Cutting is an example of a man-made inland exposure site (Figure 73). As a road cutting, the face needs periodic monitoring to determine its stability. The site is not subject to any immediate threats but vegetation may obscure rock faces over a period of years.

At some road cutting sites, stabilisation is provided by rock bolts which help to maintain friction between adjoining blocks of rock. Drains, which divert water from the top of the section, may also be installed to help stability (as water running between blocks would lead to high water pressure, and so cause slippage).

The issue of safety for people examining the rock faces at road cuttings is important when considering the open access to such sites, particularly on busy roads. Regular monitoring of

Figure 75. (a) *A river cliff of the outermost part of a meander of the River Dee, between Holt and Worthenbury. The shape of the meander continues to change as the cliff is eroded. Photo: S. Campbell.*
(b) *Meanders of the Dee viewed from the air. Photo: National Remote Sensing Centre Limited (Air Photo Group).*

road cutting sites by local authorities ensures that they are safe. A number of recent publications encouraging good practice and a wider awareness by site users appear to have been effective in reducing the incidence of damage, such as that caused by rock coring.

Site excavation and specimen curation

The excavation in Brighstone Bay, Isle of Wight

After the initial discovery in 1992 of dinosaur bones weathering out from the cliff face at Brighstone in rocks called the Wessex Formation, funds for excavation were obtained from English Nature and the Curry Fund of the Geologists' Association. The initial dig lasted about a month and enlisted much local help (Figure 74). Approximately 30% of a medium-sized dinosaur skeleton was carefully exposed, numbered, plotted, photographed, plastered and transported back to the museum premises on the Isle of Wight.

Conservation of active geomorphological process sites

Conservation of the River Dee: a mobile meander belt

The River Dee (Figure 75) is one of only a few, large rivers with a well-developed, mobile meander belt in its lower course that is relatively free from direct human intervention. The

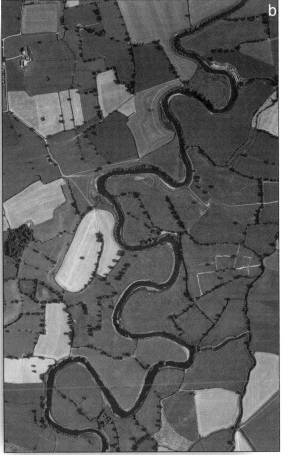

pattern and scale of the meanders at this site are exceptional. Tortuous, double-horseshoe meander bends are sustained over a relatively long distance between Holt and Worthenbury. There has also been considerable channel change by meander

Figure 76. *The rock piles at Writhlington Rock Store SSSI are an important source of plant and insect fossils. Photo: C. D. Prosser.*

migration and cut-off during historical times. This can be clearly seen on old maps of the area which show the English–Welsh border as it followed the river along a completely different course.

This locality includes both active and static geomorphological features of scientific importance in its active and abandoned channels (palaeochannels). By studying rivers like the Dee, a clearer picture of erosion and deposition processes, and meander development, can be gained, which can be important in understanding how rivers modify the landscape through time.

The main objectives in conserving this site are to maintain the fossil landforms (the valley, various ancient river cliffs, palaeochannels and abandoned meanders) in as natural a state as possible, and to allow the presently active natural processes of erosion and deposition of sediment to continue with minimal intervention, thereby allowing the channel to undergo natural changes which include meander migration. The boundary of this site is therefore sufficiently large to allow for future river channel changes.

Potential threats include river management works, such as bank maintenance, the construction of flood defence structures and floodwater management, which prevents the natural development of the floodplain. There is some evidence to suggest that the meander belt is not as active as it once was, which may be the result of river management upstream, particularly the regulation of discharges.

Large-scale river management works, which either modify the meanders or completely stabilise parts of the reach, must, therefore, be viewed as highly undesirable. In both a morphological sense (the alteration of the shape or form of the landforms) and a dynamic sense (having unquantifiable effects downstream in terms of erosion and deposition).

Mine dumps

Writhlington Rock Store SSSI

Writhlington Rock Store was nearly buried as part of a landscaping scheme, but with the co-operation of British Coal, and assistance from the Curry Fund of the Geologists' Association and English Nature, a section of the spoil was left untouched. The rock contains rare plant and insect fossils from the Carboniferous Period, and the continued access to the material has encouraged a great many important finds to be made by professional palaeontologists and amateur collectors (Figure 76). These finds have significantly enhanced our understanding of the evolution and diversity of Carboniferous insects. The area is regularly turned by machinery to expose new spoil especially for collectors.

Site 'burial'

The deliberate burial of a site, which contains sensitive or unique material susceptible to weathering or over-collection, is another practical method of Earth heritage conservation. Similarly, it may be desirable to leave a site naturally covered by

Figure 77. *The sign board at Hunstanton, Norfolk. Photo: C. D. Prosser.*

soil/vegetation (as is the case at the Rhynie Chert site, Figure 46). If the site contains sediment which is unconsolidated, natural vegetative cover may help to diminish the effects of weathering and erosion. In these examples the occasional excavation of the sites for research may be desirable.

Publicity and public awareness

Achieving recognition of a site with regard to its importance to conservation is possible through education and site publicity. This is also part of conservation, as is encouraging the 'use' of the site for scientific research or education and training. This can be done in a number of ways, including erecting information sign boards on site (Figure 77), media publicity and producing books and leaflets about particular sites or groups of sites. Of course, SSSI status does not automatically imply open access to private land, however.

Advice on conservation of Earth heritage sites

For Geological Conservation Review sites and SSSIs, local planning authorities, statutory bodies, potential developers and owners and occupiers should seek the advice of the appropriate local office of the relevant statutory nature conservation body before authorising or carrying out a potentially harmful activity at the site, or when planning any improvement to the site. The various offices of the bodies, and the areas they cover, are given in the Appendix to this book.

Further guidance on practical site conservation is given in *A Handbook of Earth Science Conservation Techniques* (the appendices to *Earth Science Conservation in Great Britain — A Strategy*).

Chapter 7

The Geological Conservation Review in the context of the wider Earth heritage conservation effort

Progress and developments in Earth heritage conservation

One of the aims of this volume has been to show that Great Britain contains a varied, fascinating and scientifically invaluable Earth heritage, which also contributes a great deal to Britain's landscape, wildlife, economy and scenic beauty. Our Earth heritage is, therefore, not only a scientific resource, but also a part of our economic, cultural and ecological inheritance.

Countless geologists, professional and amateur, have sharpened their scientific minds by studying the rocks and landscapes of Britain. As a result, many conceptual advances in the Earth sciences were made here. It might be argued that all of the sites which have played a significant part in the development of the Earth sciences should be conserved. This would be impractical. Thus the conservation of the Earth heritage resource of Great Britain has focused on selecting a series of sites that geologists consider important for the Geological Conservation Review.

For the first time it has been possible to take stock of the geological resource of Britain in a comprehensive way using standard criteria. The published results of the Geological Conservation Review provide not only a thorough science-based foundation for practical Earth heritage conservation within the series of notified Sites of Special Scientific Interest, but also a comprehensive account of the geology and geomorphology of Britain.

Earth heritage conservation strategy

In 1990, the Nature Conservancy Council published *Earth Science Conservation in Great Britain — A Strategy,* which provided a detailed and practical guide to meeting the challenge of Earth heritage conservation. It gave an overview of the problems that needed to be addressed, the means by which conservation can be effected, and the organisations best placed to take an active role. It provided a platform for taking Earth heritage conservation forward. Since its publication, the majority of its themes have been carried out successfully and developed, and have made valuable contributions to the conservation and promotion of our Earth heritage.

The strategy highlighted six areas for action:

❑ maintaining the SSSI series through the mechanism of the Geological Conservation Review

❑ expanding the RIGS network
❑ developing conservation techniques
❑ improving documentation and conservation of geological samples
❑ increasing public awareness
❑ developing international links.

Since 1990, there have been changing emphases on the approaches to Earth heritage conservation. The creation of new conservation agencies, the Countryside Council for Wales, English Nature, Scottish Natural Heritage and the Joint Nature Conservation Committee, has provided a new institutional framework. Increased public awareness and participation in local groups, the expanding RIGS network, the growth of geological leisure pursuits, the incorporation of geological sites into local authority plans and the development of new conservation techniques, have all influenced the ways in which Earth heritage conservation is perceived. The latest developments regard the Earth heritage as an integral part of our natural heritage.

For the continuing success of Earth heritage conservation strategies, it is important that all sectors of the community participate. This requires the involvement of local authorities and other statutory bodies, landowners and site managers, Earth science societies, museums, county wildlife trusts and other local and national conservation bodies, the higher education sector, schools and field centres and, of course, the general public. It is hoped that industry, which relies upon raw materials, and public utilities, which use the resources of the land and water, will continue to support the aims of Earth heritage conservation.

Progress and developments in earth heritage conservation

Maintaining the SSSI series through the mechanism of the Geological Conservation Review

As our understanding of geology and geomorphology changes with the insights provided by new discoveries and advances in Earth science theory, so new sites may need to be considered as Earth heritage SSSIs. Moreover, if a site has deteriorated or been lost, a replacement will need to be identified and notified in its place. The mechanism of the

Geological Conservation Review and its criteria are still applied when new or replacement sites are being considered. In view of this, the existing Geological Conservation Review blocks and networks will need to be reviewed and updated from time to time.

In the years since the strategy was published, it has become clear that future developments in statutory Earth heritage conservation will probably require attention to focus on a number of new areas, such as culturally and historically important sites, soils, hydrogeology and sea-bed localities.

Expanding the RIGS network

Interest in sites outside the SSSI framework of statutory protection is increasing and there is already a recognised need to mobilise voluntary bodies to take responsibility for sites of regional importance, such as RIGS. Greater participation in local groups has extended the RIGS networks, and this has been accompanied by an increase in geological leisure pursuits. There are now active RIGS groups in all the counties in England and Wales, and many in Scotland.

Developing conservation techniques

As well as developing and refining Earth heritage conservation practice (*see* Chapter 6), recent developments to find technical solutions to key problems threatening sites include the investigation and evaluation of 'soft' engineering techniques to reduce coastal erosion, as alternatives to 'hard coastal defences' that can obscure geological exposures and disrupt the transport of sediment along coasts. New engineering and blasting techniques are also being developed which can provide safe, stable exposures of rocks. Similarly, landfill schemes, which are sympathetic to the need for Earth heritage site conservation, have been further refined, so that the requirements of society are balanced with the need for conserving rock outcrops for study.

Quaternary geology can help us to understand the effects of processes such as climate change and its interaction with ecology. This knowledge can assist us in planning conservation responses in a changing world.

Geomorphologists with their specialist knowledge of active sites have an important role to play in the development of new conservation

approaches. They can advise on the practical use and management of natural resources, based on a sound understanding of geomorphological principles, and the physical and chemical changes which are taking place as the result of interaction between human land use and natural systems.

Improving documentation

Besides Geological Conservation Review publications, a programme of preparing site management plans (*see* Chapter 6) for all Earth science sites is continuing. These are designed to assist local staff in the statutory nature conservation agencies to appreciate the Earth heritage significance of sites and to enable them to pursue ways of enhancing the scientific and cultural values of sites in the light of any threats. Publications with wider appeal are also being produced, which will contribute to a greater public awareness of Britain's Earth heritage.

Increasing public awareness

There is need for a greater public understanding and awareness of environmental matters. The place of Earth science conservation in nature conservation needs greater and continuing exposure, through education and joint action.

The increasing circulation of the magazine *Earth Heritage* (formerly *Earth Science Conservation*) indicates an enhanced awareness of Earth heritage issues. This is a reflection of the publication of articles with more popular appeal; also, there is a general increase in the place of Earth heritage issues on the wider conservation scene. The series of publications *Landscape Fashioned by Geology,* published by Scottish Natural Heritage in association with the British Geological Survey, aims to describe Scotland's geology in more accessible terms and is a model for others to follow.

Since 1990, two national conferences have considered specific problems of conserving our Ice Age heritage ('Evolving landforms and Ice Age Heritage', held in May 1992 in Crewe) and the special needs of mineralogical sites ('Conserving Britain's Mineralogical Heritage', held at Manchester University in March 1992).

At a site-specific level, a number of information boards and interpretation panels have now been erected at sites across Britain to carry messages to the public; more will follow.

Developing international links

Throughout the United Kingdom, and indeed internationally, there is a growing interest in Earth heritage conservation. As well as the national conferences mentioned above, there have been two international meetings, at Digne, in France (1991), and Great Malvern (1993).

A debate on the merits of developing international guidelines to address geological and landscape conservation issues was held at the Malvern Conference and is continuing via an international group, the 'Malvern Task Force'. A central issue (which is directly relevant to the Geological Conservation Review) is that of protecting and managing internationally important sites to agreed international standards.

These activities take place in a context of increasing environmental awareness and action following the United Nations Conference on Environment and Development (UNCED) at Rio de Janeiro in 1992. They reflect a growing awareness of the interdependence between the well-being of the Earth and its peoples.

Earth heritage and nature conservation

The Rio Conference gave an impetus to efforts to manage natural resources in a sustainable way. As a result, attention is focused on the management of natural ecosystems to prevent environmental deterioration.

For example, sediments from catchments and coastal cliffs are naturally transported into the coastal zone, and these are essential for the maintenance of sand dunes, beaches, mud flats and saltmarshes. Linking into the coastal system is the fluvial transport system, where sediment is carried from a river catchment area to the floodplain, estuary and adjacent sea areas. The artificial stabilisation of any part of these dynamic natural processes could drastically interfere with their balance and so impoverish the natural environment.

Recent geological history, hydrology, soil type and soil moisture, topography and aspect all influence plant and animal habitats. The herb-rich grassland vegetation characteristic of the many upland limestone areas is very different from the moorland and bog vegetation which develops on upland acid soils overlying sandstone or granite. Any alteration to the acidity of these soils and their patterns of drainage can have fundamental effects on their local ecosystems.

These examples show how important it is to understand 'whole' systems and the relationships between processes at work in the Earth and life sciences. English Nature has developed a concept based on the identification in England of *Natural Areas*. These are defined largely on the basis of their underlying geology, landforms and soils, together with the characteristic natural vegetation types and wildlife species they support. This concept will provide a new foundation for establishing conservation objectives based on the 'whole-environment' approach to which local people can contribute. A parallel series of Natural Areas, based largely on sediment erosion, transport and deposition systems, has been developed for coastal regions in England. In Scotland, Scottish Natural Heritage is developing a similar concept using geology, landforms and soils to identify a series of biogeographic zones. The importance of soils, somewhat neglected hitherto in nature conservation, is now gaining increased prominence and their study within the concept of sustainability is likely to become an important task for the future. In Wales, the Countryside Council for Wales is also developing a landscape strategy to integrate geological, geomorphological and biological conservation, allied to public awareness and enjoyment.

Today, in the light of international, national and local activities dedicated to the conservation of the Earth heritage of Britain, it is now possible to take effective steps to safeguard the legacy of the past for future generations. The Geological Conservation Review has made this possible.

Appendix

COUNTRYSIDE COUNCIL FOR WALES

Headquarters Offices

Plas Penrhos,
Ffordd Penrhos,
Bangor,
Gwynedd
LL57 2LQ
(01248) 370444
Fax (01248) 355782

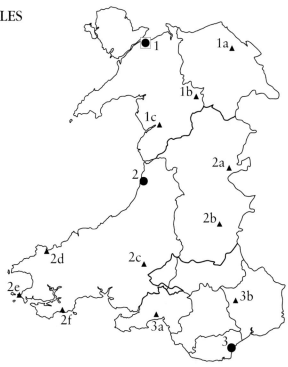

◉ Headquarters

● Regional Offices

▲ Local Offices

Regional and Local Offices

1   North Wales Region

    Bangor — North West Area

    Bryn Menai, Holyhead Road,
    Bangor, Gwynedd LL57 2EF
    (01248) 373100, Fax (01248) 370734

1a   Mold — North East Area

    Victoria House, Grosvenor Street,
    Mold, Clwyd CH7 1EJ
    (01352) 754000, Fax (01352) 752346

1b   Bala — North East Area

    Midland Bank Chambers, 56 High Street,
    Bala, Gwynedd LL23 7AB
    (01678) 521226, Fax (01678) 752346

1c   Dolgellau — North West Area

    Victoria Buildings, Meurig Street,
    Dolgellau, Gwynedd LL40 1LR
    (01341) 423750

2. Dyfed — Mid Wales Region

    Aberystwyth — West Area

    Plas Gogerddan, Aberystwyth,
    Dyfed SY23 3EE
    (01970) 828551, Fax (01970) 828314

2a Newtown — East Area

    First Floor, Ladywell House,
    Park Street, Newtown,
    Powys SY15 1RD
    (01686) 626799, Fax (01686) 629556

2b Llandrindod Wells — East Area

    3rd Floor, The Gwalia, Ithon Road,
    Llandrindod Wells, Powys
    LD1 6AA
    (01597) 824661, Fax (01597) 825734

2c Llandeilo — West Area

    Yr Hen Bost,
    56 Rhos Maen Street,
    Llandeilo, Dyfed SA19 6HA
    (01558) 822111, Fax (01558) 823467

2d Fishguard — West Area

    Sycamore Lodge, Hamilton Street,
    Fishguard, Dyfed SA65 9HL
    (01348) 874602, Fax (01348) 873936

2e Martin's Haven — West Area

    Skomer Marine Nature Reserve,
    Fishermen's Cottage, Martin's Haven,
    Haverfordwest, Dyfed SA62 3BJ
    (01646) 636736, Fax (01646) 636744

2f Stackpole — West Area

    Stackpole Home Farm, Stackpole,
    Nr Pembroke, Pembrokeshire SA71 5DQ
    (01646) 661368

3   South Wales Region

    Cardiff — South Area

    Unit 4, Castleton Court,
    Fortran Road, St Mellons,
    Cardiff CF3 0LT
    (01222) 772400, Fax (01222) 772412

3a Swansea — South Area

    RVB House, Llys Felin Newydd,
    Phoenix Way, Swansea Enterprise Park,
    Llansamlet, Swansea SA7 9FG
    (01792) 771949, Fax (01792) 771981

3b Abergavenny — East Area

    Unit 13B, Mill Street Industrial Estate,
    Abergavenny, Gwent NP7 5HE
    (01873) 857938, Fax (01873) 857938

ENGLISH NATURE

Head Office

Northminster House,
Northminster,
Peterborough
PE1 1UA

(01733) 340345
Fax (01733) 68834

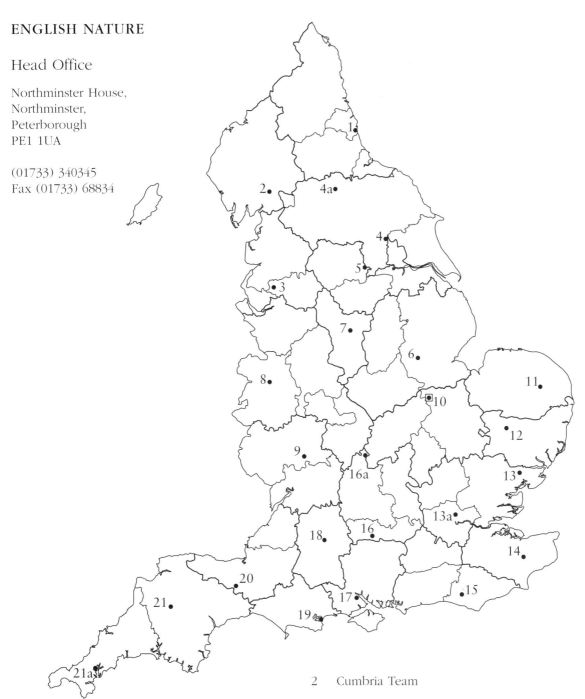

Local Area Teams

1 Northumbria Team (Northumberland,
Durham, Tyne & Wear and Cleveland)

Archbold House, Archbold Terrace,
Newcastle-upon-Tyne NE2 1EG
(0191) 281 6316, Fax (0191) 281 6305

2 Cumbria Team

Blackwell, Bowness-on-Windermere,
Windermere, Cumbria LA23 3JR
(015394) 45286, Fax (015394) 88432

3 North West Team (Lancashire, Merseyside
and Greater Manchester)

Pier House, Wallgate,
Wigan, Lancashire WN3 4AL
(01942) 820342, Fax (01942) 820364

4   North & East Yorkshire Team (includes North Humberside)

Institute for Applied Biology,
University of York,
York YO1 5DD
(01904) 432700, Fax (01904) 432705

4a Leyburn Office (Yorkshire Dales)

Thornborough Hall, Leyburn,
North Yorkshire DL8 5AB
(01969) 23447, Fax (01969) 24190

5   Humber to Pennines Team (South & West Yorkshire & South Humberside)

Bullring House, Northgate,
Wakefield, West Yorkshire
WF1 3BJ
(01924) 387010, Fax (01924) 201507

6   East Midlands Team (Leicestershire, Lincolnshire & Nottinghamshire)

The Maltings, Wharf Road,
Grantham, Lincolnshire NG31 6BH
(01476) 68431, Fax (01476) 70927

7   Peak District & Derbyshire Team

Manor Barn, Over Haddon,
Bakewell, Derbyshire DE45 1JE
(01629) 815095, Fax (01629) 815091

8   West Midlands Team (Cheshire, Shropshire, Staffordshire, Warwickshire & West Midlands)

Attingham Park, Shrewsbury,
Shropshire SY4 4TW
(01743) 709611, Fax (01743) 709303

8a Banbury Office (Warwickshire)

10/11 Butchers Row, Banbury,
Oxfordshire OX16 8JH
(01295) 257601

9   Three Counties Team (Gloucestershire & Hereford and Worcester)

Masefield House, Wells Road,
Malvern Wells, Worcestershire
WR14 4PA
(01684) 560616, Fax (01684) 893435

10 Bedfordshire, Cambridgeshire & Northamptonshire Team

Ham Lane House, Ham Lane,
Orton Waterville, Peterborough PE2 5UR
(01733) 391100, Fax (01733) 394093

11 Norfolk Team

60 Bracondale, Norwich,
Norfolk NR1 2BE
(01603) 620558, Fax (01603) 762552

12 Suffolk Team

Norman Tower House, 1-2 Crown Street,
Bury St Edmunds, Suffolk IP33 1QX
(01284) 762218, Fax (01284) 764318

13 Essex, Hertfordshire & London Team

Harbour House, Hythe Quay,
Colchester, Essex CO2 8JF
(01206) 796666, Fax (01206) 794466

13a London Office

Room 801, Chancery Lane,
Chancery House, London WC2A 1QU
(0171) 831 6922, Fax (0171) 404 3369

14 Kent Team

The Countryside Management Centre,
Coldharbour Farm, Wye
Ashford, Kent TN25 5DB
(01233) 812525, Fax (01233) 812520

15 Sussex & Surrey Team

Howard House, 31 High Street,
Lewes, East Sussex BN7 2LU
(01273) 476595, Fax (01273) 483063

16 Thames & Chilterns Team (Berkshire, Buckinghamshire & Oxfordshire)

Foxhold House, Crookham Common,
Thatcham, Berkshire RG19 8EL
(01635) 268881, Fax (01635) 268940

17 Hampshire and Isle of Wight Team

1 Southampton Road, Lyndhurst,
Hampshire SO43 7BU
(01703) 283944, Fax (01703) 283834

18   Wiltshire Team

Prince Maurice Court, Hambleton Avenue,
Devizes, Wiltshire SN10 2RT
(01380) 726344, Fax (01380) 721411

19   Dorset Team

Slepe Farm, Arne,
Wareham, Dorset BH20 5BN
(01929) 556688, Fax (01929) 554752

20   Somerset & Avon Team

Roughmoor, Bishop's Hull,
Taunton, Somerset TA1 5AA
(01823) 283211, Fax (01823) 272978

21   Devon & Cornwall Team

The Old Mill House, 37 North Street,
Okehampton, Devon EX20 1AR
(01837) 55045, Fax (01837) 55046

21a Cornwall Office

Trelissick, Feock,
Truro, Cornwall TR3 6QL
(01872) 865261, Fax (01872) 865534

SCOTTISH NATURAL HERITAGE

Headquarters Offices

*Secretariat, Resources Directorate,
Policy Directorate, Communications
Directorate*

12 Hope Terrace, Edinburgh,
EH9 2AS
(0131) 447 4784
Fax (0131) 446 2277

*Research and Advisory Services
Directorate, Information and Library
Services*

2 Anderson Place,
Edinburgh EH6 5NP
(0131) 447 4784
Fax (0131) 446 2405

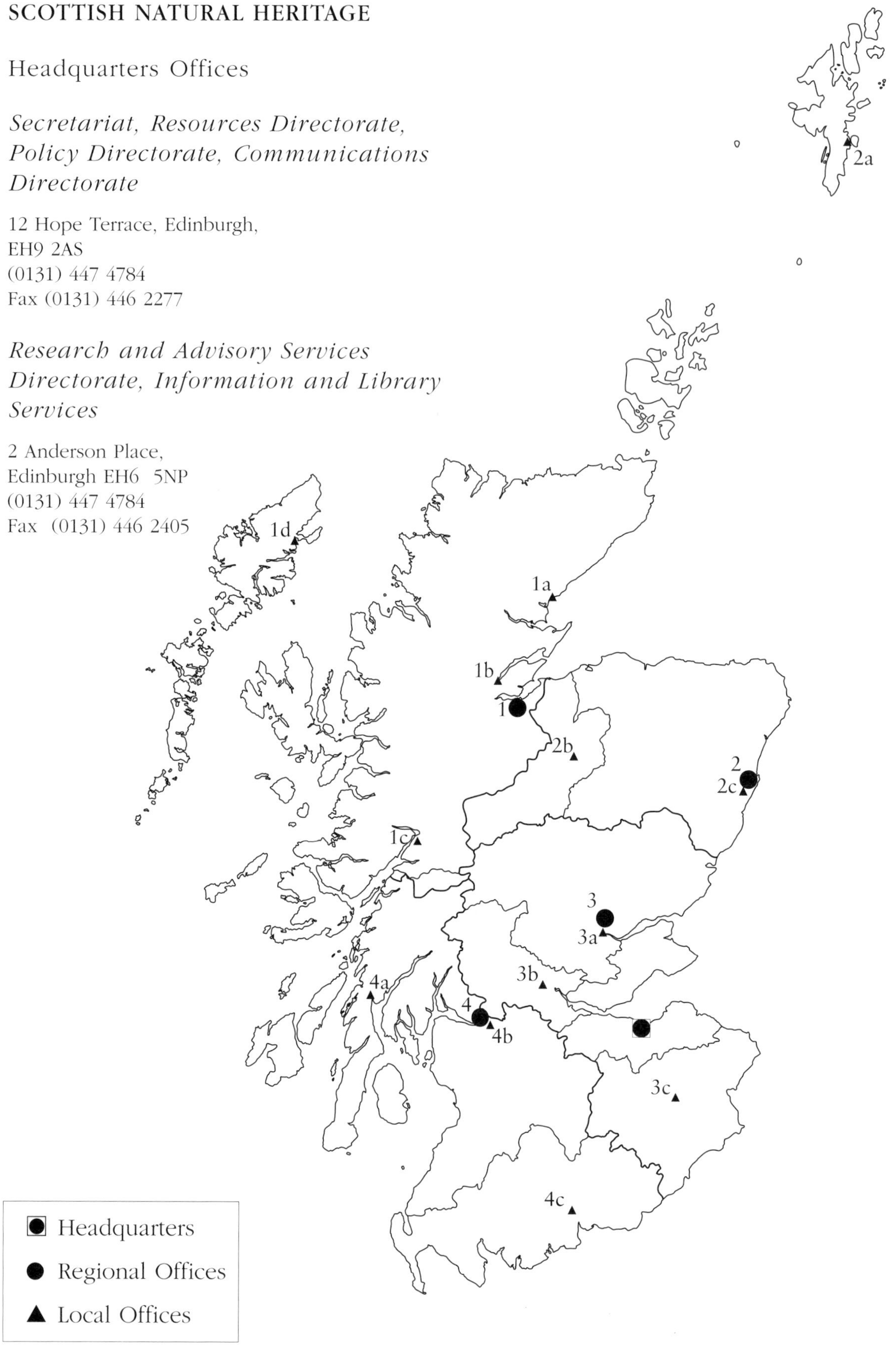

2a

1d

1a

1b

1

2b

2
2c

1c

3
3a

3b

4a

4
4b

3c

4c

◉ Headquarters

● Regional Offices

▲ Local Offices

Appendix

Regional and Local Offices

1 North West Region

Fraser Darling House, 9 Culduthel Road,
Inverness IV2 4AG
(01463) 239431, Fax (01463) 710713

1a Caithness and Sutherland Area

Main Street, Golspie,
Sutherland KW10 6TG
(01408) 633602, Fax (01408) 633071

1b Ross & Cromarty and Inverness Area

Fodderty Way, Dingwall Business Park,
Dingwall IV15 9XB
(01349) 865333, Fax (01349) 865609

1c Lochaber & Skye and Lochalsh Area

Mamore House, The Parade,
Fort William, Inverness-shire PH33 6BA
(01397) 704716, Fax (01397) 700303

1d Western Isles Area

32 Francis Street, Stornoway,
Isle of Lewis HS1 2ND
(01851) 705258, Fax (01851) 704900

2 North East Region

Wynne-Edwards House, 17 Rubislaw Terrace,
Aberdeen AB1 1XE
(01224) 642863, Fax (01224) 643347

2a Northern Isles Area

2-4 Alexandra Building, The Esplanade,
Lerwick, Shetland ZE1 0LL
(01595) 693345, Fax (01595) 692565

2b Strathspey Area

Achantoul, Aviemore,
Inverness-shire PH22 1QD
(01479) 810477, Fax (01479) 811363

2c East Grampian Area

48 Queen's Road, Aberdeen AB1 6YE
(01224) 312266, Fax (01224) 311366

3 South East Region

Battleby, Redgorton,
Perth PH1 3EW
(01738) 444177, Fax (01738) 444180

3a Tayside Area

55 York Place, Perth,
PH2 8EH
(01738) 639746, Fax (01738) 442060

3b Central and Fife Area

The Beta Centre,
Innovation Park,
University of Stirling,
Stirling FK9 4NF
(01786) 450362, Fax (01786) 451974

3c Lothian and Borders Area

Anderson's Chambers, Market Street,
Galashiels TD1 3AF
(01896) 756652, Fax (01896) 750427

4 South West Region

Caspian House, Mariner Court,
Clydebank Business Park,
Clydebank G81 2NR
(0141) 9514488, Fax (0141) 9514510

4a Argyll and Bute Area

1 Kilmory Industrial Estate,
Kilmory, Lochgilphead,
Argyll PA31 8RR
(01546) 603611, Fax (01546) 602298

4b Mid and South Strathclyde Area

Caspian House, Mariner Court,
Clydebank Business Park, Clydebank
G81 2NR
(0141) 951 4488, Fax (0141) 951 8948

4c Dumfries and Galloway Area

Carmont House,
Crichton Royal Estate,
Bankend Road,
Dumfries DG1 4UQ
(01387) 247010, Fax (01387) 259247

References and further reading

GEOLOGICAL CONSERVATION REVIEW SERIES

Benton, M.J. and Spencer, P.S. (1995) *Fossil Reptiles of Great Britain*. GCR Series No.10, Chapman & Hall, London, 386pp.

Bridgland, D.R. (1994) *Quaternary of the Thames*. GCR Series No.7, Chapman & Hall, London, 441pp.

Campbell, S. (ed.) (in press) *Quaternary of South-west England*. GCR Series, Chapman & Hall, London.

Campbell, S. and Bowen, D.Q. (1989) *Quaternary of Wales*. GCR Series No.2, Nature Conservancy Council, Peterborough, 237pp.

Cleal, C.J. and Thomas, B.A. (1996) *British Upper Carboniferous Stratigraphy*. GCR Series No.11, Chapman & Hall, London, 339pp.

Cleal, C.J. and Thomas, B.A. (1995) *Palaeozoic Palaeobotany of Great Britain*. GCR Series No.9, Chapman & Hall, London, 295pp.

Emeleus, C.H. and Gyopari, M.C. (1992) *British Tertiary Volcanic Province*. GCR Series No.4, Chapman & Hall, London, 259pp.

Floyd, P.A., Exley, C.S. and Styles, M.T. (1993) *Igneous Rocks of South West England*. GCR Series No.5, Chapman & Hall, London, 256pp.

Gordon, J.E. and Sutherland, D.G. (eds) (1993) *Quaternary of Scotland*. GCR Series No.6, Chapman & Hall, London, 695pp.

Gregory, K.J. (ed.) (in press) *Fluvial Geomorphology of Great Britain*. GCR Series, Chapman & Hall, London.

Smith, D.B. (1995) *Marine Permian of England*. GCR Series No.8, Chapman & Hall, London, 205pp.

Treagus, J.E. (ed.) (1992) *Caledonian Structures in Britain: South of the Midland Valley*. GCR Series No.3, Chapman & Hall, London, 177pp.

Waltham, A.C., Simms, M.J., Farrant, A.J. and Goldie, H.S. (in press) *Karst and Caves of Great Britain*. GCR Series, Chapman & Hall, London.

These volumes, with the exception of *Quaternary of Wales,* can be bought from Chapman & Hall, 2–6 Boundary Row, London SE1 8HN. *Quaternary of Wales* is available from Earth Science Branch, JNCC, Monkstone House, City Road, Peterborough, PE1 1JY.

REFERENCES

Boulton, G.S. and Paul, M.A. (1976) The influence of genetic processes on some geotechnical properties of glacial tills. *Quarterly Journal of Engineering Geology,* **9**, 159–94.

Buckland, W. (1824) Notice on the *Megalosaurus,* or great fossil lizard of Stonesfield. *Transactions of the Geological Society of London,* Series 2, **1**, 390–6.

Clarkson, E.N.K., Milner, A.R. and Coates, M.I. (1994) Palaeoecology of the Visean of East Kirkton, West Lothian, Scotland. *Transactions of the Royal Society of Edinburgh, Earth Sciences,* **84**, 417–25.

Conservation Committee of the Geological Society

(1984) *Record of the Rocks*. (Leaflet available from the Geological Society, Burlington House, Piccadilly, London W1V 9AG.)

Duff, K.L., McKirdy, A.P. and Harley, M.J. (1985) *New Sites for Old*. Nature Conservancy Council, Peterborough.

Dunning, F.W., Mercer, I.F., Owen, M.P., Roberts, R.H. and Lambert, J.L.M. (1978) *Britain Before Man*. HMSO for the Institute of Geological Sciences, London, 136pp.

Edmonds, E. (1983) *The Geological Map*. HMSO for the Institute of Geological Sciences, London.

Gass, I. G, Smith, P. J. and Wilson, R.C.L. (eds) (1971) *Understanding the Earth*, Artemis Press, 355pp.

Geologists' Association. *A Code for Geological Fieldwork*. (Leaflet available from the Geologists' Association, Burlington House, Piccadilly, London W1V 9AG.)

Grayson, A. (1993) *Rock Solid*. Natural History Museum, London, 72pp.

Lovell, J.P.B. (1977) *The British Isles through Geological Time, a Northward Drift*. George Allen & Unwin, London.

National Caving Association (1995) *Cave Conservation Policy*. National Caving Association, London.

Nature Conservancy Council (1990) *Earth Science Conservation in Great Britain — A Strategy* and *Appendices — A Handbook of Earth Science Conservation Techniques*. Nature Conservancy Council, Peterborough.

Rickards, R.B. (1993) Graptolites. In *The Encyclopedia of the Solid Earth Sciences* (ed. P. Kearey). Blackwell Scientific, Oxford, 713pp.

Wilson, R.C.L. (ed.) (1994) *Earth Heritage Conservation*. The Geological Society, London in association with The Open University, Milton Keynes, 272pp.

Wyllie, P.J. (1976) *The Way the Earth Works*. John Wiley & Sons Ltd, New York, 296pp.

FURTHER READING

Stratigraphy

General reading

Hecht, J. (1995) The Geological Timescale. Inside Science Number 81. *New Scientist*, 20 May pp.1–4.

Technically advanced level

Salvador, A. (ed.) (1994) *International Stratigraphic Guide: a Guide to Stratigraphic Classification, Terminology and Procedure*, 2nd edition. International Union of Geological Sciences and the Geological Society of America, Boulder, Colorado, USA.

Whittaker, A., Cope, J.C.W., Cowie, J.W. *et al.* (1991) A guide to stratigraphical procedure. Geological Society of London Special Report No. 20, *Journal of the Geological Society, London*, **148**, 813–24.

Geology and the geology of Britain

General reading

An invaluable reference book covering all aspects of Earth heritage conservation is provided by Wilson (ed.) (1994), details of which are provided in the reference list. A personal account of the connections between the geological history of Britain and its landscapes is given by Fortey, R. (1993) *The Hidden Landscape: A Journey into the Geological Past*. Pimlico, London (paperback) 310pp. It is an extremely readable follow-up to the introduction given in Chapter 3 of this book.

A series of booklets available from the Natural History Museum (Earth Galleries), Exhibition Road, London SW7 5BD, provide a valuable source of information about geology. Titles include: *British Fossils* (three volumes)*, Volcanoes, Rock Solid* and *Britain's Offshore Oil and Gas* (published by United Kingdom Offshore Operators Association).

Titles available from the British Geological Survey include the *Holiday Geology Guides* series and *Discovering Geology* cards. They are available from British Geological Survey, Kingsley Dunham Centre, Keyworth, Nottingham NG12 5GG; Murchison House, West Mains Road, Edinburgh EH9 2LF and BGS London Information Office, Natural History Museum (Earth Galleries), Exhibition Road, London SW7 2DE.

In 1993, Scottish Natural Heritage launched a new series of booklets entitled *Landscape Fashioned by Geology*. The series is produced in association with the British Geological Survey and describes the geology of Scotland in relatively simple terms. Titles include *Edinburgh, Skye, Cairngorms* and *Loch Lomond to Stirling*.

The former Nature Conservancy Council published two booklets in the 'Making of Modern Britain' series:

Nield, T., McKirdy, A.P. and Harley, M.J. (1989) *The Age of Ice.* No. 1.

Nield, T., McKirdy, A.P. and Harley, M.J. (1990) *Death of an Ocean.* No. 2.

Advanced level

The British Geological Survey (addresses above) publishes and sells geological maps and regional geological summaries and memoirs to accompany map sheets.

Two volumes covering the geology of the whole of Britain have been published by the Geological Society, London, and are available from Geological Society Publishing House, Unit 7, Brassmill Enterprise Centre, Brassmill Lane, Bath BA1 3JN:

Craig, G.Y. (1991) *Geology of Scotland,* 3rd edition. 612pp.

Duff, P.,McL. D. and Smith, A.J. (ed) (1992) *Geology of England and Wales.* 651pp.

Earth heritage and nature conservation

The reference book *Earth Heritage Conservation* (Wilson, 1994 — *see* reference list) covers all aspects of the topic. It is available from the Geological Society Publishing House (the address is provided above). *Earth Science Conservation in Great Britain — a Strategy* and *Appendices — A Handbook of Earth Science Conservation Techniques* is available from the Headquarters offices of the county conservation agencies (see Appendix). Other publications include:

Earth Heritage (previously named *Earth Science Conservation*) A twice-yearly journal covering the wide issues relevant to geological and geomorphological conservation. Available from English Nature (*see* address in Appendix).

Geologists' Assocation (1989) *Take Care When You Core.* (Leaflet available from the Geologists' Association, Burlington House, Piccadilly, London W1V 9AG.)

Glasser, N.F. and Barber, G. (1995) Cave conservation plans: the role of English Nature. *Cave and Karst Science,* **21** (2), 33–6.

Nature Conservancy Council/English Nature (1991–1992) produced several leaflets on Earth heritage conservation principles, including *Conserving our Heritage of Rocks, Fossils and Landforms; Fossil collecting and conservation; Regionally Important Geological/geomorphological Sites;* and the series "*Earth Science conservation for ...*" (*for Landfill Managers; for Farmers and Landowners; for the Mineral Extraction Industry; for Quarry and Pit Managers; for District Planners; for Coastal Engineers,* and *for Wildlife Trusts*).

O'Halloran, D., Green, C., Harley, M., Stanley, M. and Knill, J. (eds) (1994) *Geological and Landscape Conservation.* The Geological Society, London. (Proceedings of the Malvern International Conference on Geological and Landscape Conservation, Great Malvern, 1993.)

Prosser, C.D. (1992) Active quarrying and conservation. *Earth Science Conservation,* **31**, 22–4.

Prosser, C.D. (1992) Bartonian stratotype seriously threatened. *Geology Today* September-October, 163–4.

Prosser, C. D. (1994) The role of English Nature in fossil excavation. *Geological Curator,* **6** (2), 71–4.

Stevens, C., Gordon, J.E., Green, C.P. and Macklin M.G. (eds) (1994) Proceedings of the Conference *Conserving our Landscape, Evolving Landforms and Ice-age Heritage,* Crewe, 1992. Available from English Nature.

Glossary

Alpine Orogeny: A period of mountain building resulting from the collision of the European and African **plates** which took place during the late **Tertiary Period**.

Ammonite: An extinct marine **cephalopod mollusc**; most forms had a tightly coiled, planispiral shell. Modern relatives include *Nautilus* and squids.

Andesite: A **volcanic rock**, intermediate in composition between **basalt** and **rhyolite**.

Anticline: An arch-shaped fold, with younger **strata** on the outermost part of the arch.

Aplite: A fine-grained, often light-coloured, **intrusive igneous** rock with high **silica** content, found in veins and **dykes** associated with **granite** intrusions. Aplites have a characteristic 'sugary' texture.

Arthropod: A group of invertebrates which have a segmented body and jointed limbs and an external skeleton (e.g. insects, spiders and crustaceans).

Axis (plural 'axes'): In botany, main stem or root.

Back reef: The area lying landward of a reef.

Bar: A more or less linear ridge of sand and/or gravel.

Basalt: A fine-grained, usually dark-coloured, crystalline **igneous** rock, with a **silica** content less than 53% by weight.

Batholith: A large, irregular mass of **igneous** rock emplaced deep in the Earth's **crust**.

Bed: A layer within a sequence of **sedimentary** rocks defined by planar to irregular boundaries representing an original depositional surface.

Belemnite: An extinct marine **cephalopod mollusc**, which possessed a bullet-shaped internal calcium carbonate shell. Modern relatives include *Nautilus* and squids.

Bioherm: A mound-shaped build-up of mainly *in situ* colonial organisms.

Biostratigraphy: The **stratigraphical** sub-division and **correlation** of **sedimentary** rocks based on their **fossil** content.

Biostrome: A sheet-like accumulation of **fossil** shells that are preserved in their life positions.

Bivalve: A class of **mollusc** that has two shells (valves) held together at a hinge area. Typically, the valves are symmetrical at the plane of the junction between them. Examples are oysters and mussels.

(GCR) Block: The classification unit used to select and describe sites characteristic of the geology of Great Britain.

Boulder clay: Poorly sorted, unstratified sediment, with grains ranging in size from rock 'flour' to boulders, deposited beneath **glaciers** and **ice sheets**, or from melting ice. Also referred to as 'till'.

Brachiopod: A marine organism which has two shells (valves) held together at the hinge area. Typically the valves are dissimilar, the plane of symmetry being at right angles to the plane of junction between the valves (c.f. **bivalves**).

Breccia: A coarse-grained **sedimentary** rock consisting of angular fragments.

Bryozoan: Type of aquatic colonial organism (normally marine) comprising individuals living in linked box-like skeletons composed of calcium carbonate.

Caledonian Orogeny: A major period of mountain building which took place during the Lower **Palaeozoic** sub-**Era**, associated with the closure of the ancient Iapetus Ocean situated between 'Scotland' and the rest of present-day Britain.

Cambrian: The first geological **period** of the **Palaeozoic Era** (ranging from 570 to 510 million years ago). It contains the oldest **fossils** of organisms with mineralised skeletons.

Carbonate rocks: Rock formed mostly from carbonate minerals such as calcite ($CaCO_3$) and dolomite ($CaMg(CO_3)_2$).

Carboniferous: The geological **period** ranging from 345 to 280 million years ago of the Upper **Palaeozoic** sub-**Era**.

Cauldron subsidence: A collapsed area of a volcanic crater surrounded by circular **igneous dykes**.

Cenozoic: The youngest **era** of geological time spanning from approximately 65 million years ago to the present, consisting of the **Tertiary** and **Quaternary periods**.

Cephalopod: A class of marine **mollusc** which includes the extinct **ammonites** and **belemnites**, and the living squid, cuttlefish, octopus and *Nautilus*.

Chert: A fine-grained **silica**-rich rock occurring within **sedimentary** and **volcanic rocks**.

China clay: Deposit of the mineral kaolin, produced by the alteration of granite by hot fluids deep in the Earth's **crust**, or by surface **weathering**.

Chronostratigraphic unit (Time-rock unit): A sequence of rocks deposited during a particular interval of geological time. Historically, time-rock units were defined before the units in the geological time scale. Geological time scale units were actually based on time-rock units, rather than the other way round as suggested by the definition. For example, sediments laid down during the **Ordovician Period** (a geological time unit) belong to the Ordovician **System** (a chronostratigraphic unit). The hierarchy of chronostratigraphic units consists of erathem (equivalent to era), system (period), series, stage and chronozone.

Cirque: A deep, steep-walled hollow in a mountain caused by glacial erosion; equivalent to corrie in Scotland and cwm in Wales.

Clast: A fragment of rock or a mineral grain resulting from the **erosion** and transport of **weathered** rock material.

Clay: A sediment composed of extremely small grains less than four thousandths of a millimetre across.

Conglomerate: A very coarse-grained sediment consisting of rounded **clasts**.

Conservation: Protection, preservation and careful management of natural resources and the environment.

Contact: The junction between two different rock types. The term is often used to describe the juxtaposition of **igneous** and **sedimentary** rocks and the associated **metamorphism** of the latter ('contact metamorphism').

Continental crust: The part of the Earth's **crust** that lies beneath the continents and continental shelves and that has a density 2.7 to 3.0 times that of water. It varies in thickness from 25 to 70 kilometres.

Continental drift: The relative movement of the continents during Earth history.

Core: The central part of the Earth below a depth of 2900 kilometres, thought to be composed of a mixture of nickel and iron.

Correlation: In **stratigraphy**, the establishment of a correspondence between **stratigraphic units** using either similarities in rock type or **fossil** content. Isolated sequences of rock may be correlated as being once physically continuous units, or deposited during the same span of time.

Country rock: The rock **intruded** by a **plutonic igneous** rock.

Cretaceous: The last **period** of the **Mesozoic Era**, ranging from 140 to 65 million years ago.

Crust: The thin outermost solid layer of the Earth. It varies in thickness from about 5 kilometres (beneath the oceans) to 30–70 kilometres (beneath the continents).

Cryoturbation: Movements of the ground caused by seasonal freezing and thawing above a permanently frozen zone.

Cupola: A small dome-like protuberance projecting from the main body of an **igneous intrusion**.

Cuticle: Outer protective 'skin' covering the aerial parts of most land plants. It helps to reduce water loss.

Cyano-bacteria: Blue-green algae; micro-organisms capable of **photosynthesising**. **Fossil** forms have been found in rocks more than 3000 million years old.

Debris dyke: A crevasse-like feature in the ice surface filled with glacial debris.

Denudation: The combined processes of

weathering and **erosion** that wear down landscapes. From the Latin *denudare*, to 'strip bare'.

Deposition: The accumulation of sediment in aqueous or subaerial environments.

Devonian: The first **period** of the Upper **Palaeozoic** sub-**Era**, ranging from 395 to 345 million years ago.

Dolerite: A medium-grained **intrusive igneous** rock which has the same chemical and mineralogical composition as **extrusive basalt** and **plutonic gabbro**.

Dolomite: A mineral composed of calcium-magnesium carbonate, or a rock composed of this mineral. Many dolomitic rocks are limestones that were 'dolomitised' by the action of groundwater solutions rich in magnesium.

Drift deposits: Sediments deposited from rivers, **glaciers** and **ice sheets** overlying older geological formations. Geological maps are referred to as 'drift maps' when they show such deposits, or as 'solid maps' when these deposits are omitted.

Drumlin: A streamlined, oval-shaped hill composed of **boulder clay** (and occasionally solid rock). Its long axis is parallel to the direction of flow of the **ice sheet** beneath which it formed.

Dyke: A sheet-like body of **igneous** rock that cuts across the bedding of the rocks it **intrudes**; it is often steeply inclined.

Earth heritage: The inheritance of rocks, soils and landforms (active and relict) and the evidence they contain that enables the history of the Earth to be unravelled.

Earth science: The applications of the principles and methods of mathematics, biology, chemistry, physics and those special to **Earth science**, to the study of the Earth and the elucidation of its history.

Echinoderm: Marine animals usually characterised by a five-fold symmetry, and possessing an internal skeleton of calcite plates and a complex water **vascular** system. Includes echinoids (sea urchins), crinoids (sea lilies) and asteroids (starfish).

Ecosystem: A system that encompasses the interactions between a community of organisms and its surrounding environment.

Eon: The largest unit of geological time, divided into **eras**.

Era: A large unit of geological time composed of several **periods**. The **Phanerozoic Eon** is divided into the **Palaeozoic**, **Mesozoic** and **Cenozoic** eras, and their constituent periods are defined on the basis of their characteristic content of invertebrate, vertebrate and plant **fossils**.

Erosion: The process of wearing away the Earth's surface through the removal of rock debris by water, wind and ice.

Erratic: A large clast left behind by melting ice and composed of rock not found locally.

Esker: A sinuous ridge of sand and gravel deposited by a meltwater stream flowing within a tunnel under a **glacier** or **ice sheet**.

Evaporite: A general term used to describe sediments that formed by the precipitation of salts due to the evaporation of sea or lake water.

Exposure sites: Sites whose scientific or educational value lies in providing surface exposures of geological features that are extensive or plentiful underground, but are otherwise not visible (e.g. coastal cliffs, quarries).

Extrusive rock: **Igneous** rock that originally erupted as a liquid (**magma**) at the Earth's surface.

Fault: A fracture in the Earth's **crust** along which rock units were displaced relative to one another.

Fauna: Animal life of a region or environment today, or in the past.

Feldspar: A group of aluminium-silicate rock-forming minerals. They are the most abundant minerals in the Earth's **crust**.

Fluvial: Relating to a river or river system.

Fold: A bend in rock **strata** produced by earth movements.

Fossil: The preserved remains or traces of once-living animals and plants.

Gabbro: A coarse-grained, often dark-coloured **plutonic igneous** rock.

Gastropod: A class of marine, freshwater and terrestrial **molluscs** which live in a single shell that is usually coiled.

GCR: Geological Conservation Review, in which nationally important geological and geomorphological sites were assessed and selected with a view to their long-term conservation.

Geology: The study of the Earth, its origins, structure, composition and history (including the development of life), and the nature of the processes that have given rise to its present state.

Geomorphology: The study of landforms and the processes that formed them.

Glacier: A large body of ice occupying **corries** and a valley in a mountainous area, and which moves slowly under the influence of gravity.

Glaciofluvial sediments: Sands and gravels deposited from meltwater streams associated with **ice sheets** and **glaciers**.

Glaciolacustrine: Sediments deposited in lakes marginal to a **glacier**.

Glaciotectonic: Deformation of rocks or sediments caused by **glacial** movement.

Gneiss: A coarse-grained **metamorphic** rock, composed of alternating light and dark bands, formed at very high temperatures and pressures.

Granite: A coarse-grained **plutonic igneous** rock rich in **silica**, consisting largely of **feldspar** and **quartz**.

Granodiorite: A coarse-grained **igneous** rock similar to **granite** in texture but containing slightly less **silica**.

Graptolite: Extinct colonial planktonic animals, distantly related to chordates; widely used for **Palaeozoic stratigraphical correlations**.

Greywacke: A sandstone containing more than 15% clay between the constituent **clasts**.

Gypsum: Hydrated calcium sulphate, often occurring as an **evaporite** mineral.

Hornfels: A hard, fine-grained, splintery rock, resulting from the baking of sediments in contact with **magma**.

Hydrocarbons: Naturally occurring organic compounds containing hydrogen and carbon, such as natural gas, oil and bitumen.

Hydrothermal activity: Processes associated with **igneous** activity that involve heated or superheated water.

Ice Age: Popular name often given to the **Quaternary Period** during which large areas were repeatedly covered by **ice sheets** and **glaciers**.

Ice cap: An area of ice, smaller than an **ice sheet**, occurring in the polar regions and high mountains.

Ice foliation: Thinly bedded layering in the ice.

Ice sheet: Very large areas of ice, such as those covering much of Greenland and Antarctica today. During the **Quaternary**, ice sheets covered much of the Northern Hemisphere.

Igneous rocks: Rocks formed from molten rock (**magma**). They usually consist of interlocking crystals, the size of which is dependent on the rate of cooling (slow cooling gives larger crystals; rapid cooling produces small crystals).

In situ: Latin 'in place', used to describe features and **fossils** found where they were formed.

Integrity sites: Sites whose scientific or educational value lies in the fact that they contain finite and limited deposits or **landforms** that are irreplaceable if destroyed.

Interglacial: A period of relatively warm climate between two episodes of glaciation.

Intrusive rock: Rock which, in the molten state, was forced into ('intruded') pre-existing rocks and solidified without reaching the surface.

IUGS: International Union of Geological Sciences.

JNCC: Joint Nature Conservation Committee.

Joints: A fracture in a rock that exhibits no displacement across it (unlike a **fault**). Joints may be caused by the shrinkage of **igneous** rocks as they cool in the solid state, or, in sediments, by the regional extension or compression of sediment caused by earth movements.

Jurassic: The middle of the three **periods** of the **Mesozoic Era**, ranging from 195 to 140 million years ago.

Kame: A mound of sand and gravel originally deposited on top of a **glacier** or **ice sheet** by meltwaters, and remaining as a topographic feature after the ice melted.

Karst: Landscape produced by the dissolution of limestones by percolating groundwaters and underground streams. Named after the Karst region of the former Yugoslavia.

Kettle hole: A depression in glacial or **glaciofluvial** sediments, resulting from the melting of a mass of **glacier** ice that was buried in sediment.

Landform: A natural feature of the surface of the land.

Lava: Molten rock **extruded** onto the Earth's surface, or the resultant solid rock.

Limestone: A **sedimentary** rock composed of calcium carbonate (calcite), often derived from the shells of organisms.

Limestone pavement: A bare limestone surface formed by solution processes that enlarge joints to produce ridges ('clints') and clefts ('grykes').

Lithification: A general term used to describe the conversion of sediment into rock.

Lithology: The term encompassing the colour, size and shape of constituent crystals or **clasts**, and the mineral composition of a rock.

Lithostratigraphy: The **stratigraphical** sub-division and **correlation** of **sedimentary**

rocks based on their **lithological** features.

Lodgement till: A glacial deposit laid down underneath an **ice sheet** or valley **glacier**. It is usually clay-rich and contains boulders.

Machair: Dune pasture with lime-rich soil.

Magma: Molten rock; referred to as **lava** when extruded onto the Earth's surface.

Maniraptor: A group of small, bipedal carnivorous dinosaurs.

Mantle: The layer of the Earth's interior situated between the **core** and the **crust**. It is about 2300 kilometres thick.

Marl: A calcareous **clay** or mudstone.

Mass extinction: The dying-out of several plant and/or animal groups over a brief period of geological time.

Mass movement: The down-slope movement of rock debris or sediment under the influence of gravity.

Mesozoic: The middle of the three **eras** that constitute the **Phanerozoic Eon**. Literal meaning is 'middle life', it spans the **Triassic** to the **Tertiary**, from 230 to 65 million years ago.

Metallogenetic: Containing metallic mineral deposits or **ores**.

Metamorphic rocks: Rocks which have been changed in the solid state by heat and/or pressure, without melting. They may originally have been either **igneous** or **sedimentary** rocks. Examples include slate (changed from **clay**) and marble (originally **limestone**).

Mineral: A naturally occurring chemical compound or element.

Mineralogy: The study of minerals.

Molluscs: Invertebrates with a fleshy soft body and, usually, a hard shell. May be marine, freshwater or terrestrial; includes **gastropods** (snails, limpets), **bivalves** (oysters, mussels), **cephalopods** etc.

Moraine: Ridges of unsorted, unstratified glacial **till** deposited on top of or at the margins of a **glacier** or **ice sheet**.

Nautilus: A living **cephalopod mollusc** with a coiled external shell, related to the squid and octopus.

NCC: Nature Conservancy Council.

(GCR) Network: A conceptual framework of geological characteristics which encompasses the Earth science features of a **block**; a block may contain one or more networks.

New Red Sandstone: A sequence of red, largely desert and **fluvial** sediments, which were formed in Britain after the **Carboniferous Period**, but before the **Jurassic**.

Oceanic crust: The part of the Earth's **crust** that lies beneath the ocean basins, varying in thickness between 6 and 11 kilometres, and composed largely of **basalt** and **gabbro**.

Oil shale: A dark-grey or black shale which contains organic substances that yield **hydrocarbons**, but does not contain free petroleum.

Old Red Sandstone: A sequence of red continental (largely **fluvial**) sediments in Britain of **Devonian** age.

Ooid: A spherical/ subspherical carbonate-coated **sedimentary** particle, less than 2 millimetres in diameter.

Ordovician: The second **period** in the **Palaeozoic Era**, ranging from 510 to 439 million years ago.

Ore: A mineral or rock that can be exploited commercially.

Orogeny: A mountain-building period, during which **continental crust** is thickened by processes associated with the closing of oceans and subsequent collision between continents.

Outcrop: An area of rock which is naturally exposed at the Earth's surface.

Outwash sediments: Sands and gravels deposited by streams beyond the ice margin. These streams originate within and beneath the ice, and transport the sediments to locations 'outside' the margin.

Palaeobotany: the study of the fragmentary fossilised remains of plants.

Palaeochannel: A 'fossil' river or tidal channel (i.e. one that is no longer active).

Palaeontology: The study of **fossil** fauna and flora, including their evolution and reconstruction of past animal communities and ancient environments.

Palaeozoic: The first of the three **eras** of the **Phanerozoic Eon**. Literal meaning 'old life', it spans the **Cambrian** to the **Permian periods**, from 570 to 230 million years ago. The era is sometimes divided into sub-eras, the Lower Palaeozoic (**Cambrian** to **Silurian** Periods) and the Upper Palaeozoic (**Devonian** to **Permian** periods).

Pangaea: A supercontinent that existed more than 200 million years ago, before being fragmented by **continental drift**.

Patch reef: An isolated body reef or body of reef rock.

Pegmatite: A very coarsely crystalline **igneous** rock, with crystals greater than 3 centimetres in length that formed during the final stages of cooling of a large volume of **magma**.

Peridotite: A coarsely crystalline, **silica**-poor, **igneous** rock consisting predominantly of the mineral olivine. The Earth's **mantle** is probably composed largely of peridotite.

Periglacial: A term applied to the region adjacent to a **glacier**. The ground is largely permanently frozen, but may thaw during the summer.

Period: A geological time scale unit (c.f. system, a **chronostratigraphic** (time-rock) unit).

Permian: The last **period** of the **Palaeozoic Era**, ranging from 280 to 230 million years ago.

Petrology: The study of the composition, occurrence and origin of rocks.

Phanerozoic: An **eon** comprising the **Cenozoic**, **Mesozoic** and **Palaeozoic eras**.

Photosynthesis: The process by which the energy of sunlight is used by organisms, especially green plants, to synthesise carbohydrates from carbon dioxide and water.

Pillow lava: Rounded masses of **basaltic lava** formed by **extrusion** under water.

Plate: A rigid 'slab' of the Earth's **crust** and uppermost **mantle** that moves relative to other plates.

Pluton: A general term for a deep-seated **igneous intrusion**, irrespective of its size.

Precambrian: An informal term to encompass all of the time that precedes the **Phanerozoic Eon** (i.e. 4600 to 570 million years ago).

Prograding shoreline: The seaward migration of a shoreline.

Proterozoic: The second **eon** of geological time, forming the later part of the '**Precambrian**'.

Quartz: A mineral composed entirely of **silica**.

Quartzite: A **metamorphic** rock formed from pure **quartz** sandstones.

Quaternary: The latest **period** of geological time, from 1.6 million years ago to the present. (*See* 'Ice Age'.)

Radiometric dating: Methods of dating certain rocks or minerals using the relative abundances of radioactive and stable isotopes of certain elements, together with known rates of decay of radioactive elements. Radiocarbon dates extend back to only 50,000 years, but other elements (potassium, lead, uranium) are used to obtain dates in the order of tens to thousands of millions of years.

Raised beach: A former beach now situated above the level of the present shoreline as a result of earth movement or changes in global sea level or land level.

Reef crest: The top of the seaward slope of a reef.

Reef flat: The relatively flat area behind the **reef crest**.

(Marine) Regression: The withdrawal of water from parts of the land surface as a result of a fall in sea level relative to the land.

Relict: Descriptive of a geological feature surviving in its primitive form.

Rhyolite: A fine-grained lava, having the same chemical and mineralogical compositions as granite.

RIGS: Regionally Important Geological/ geomorphological Sites.

Rock: A mass of mineral matter that may or may not be **lithified**.

Roof pendant: A mass of **country rock** immediately above an **igneous** rock body.

Sabkha: The Arabic word for a wide area of coastal flats bordering a lagoon. **Evaporite** minerals are formed in such areas.

Sandstone: A **sedimentary** rock made of **lithified** sand.

Sauropod: Quadrapedal, herbivorous dinosaurs of the **Jurassic** and **Cretaceous periods**. Examples include *Diplodocus* and *Brachiosaurus*.

Schist: **Metamorphic** rock characterised by the parallel alignment of constituent minerals, commonly the platy mineral mica.

Scree: See 'Talus'.

Sediment: Loose material derived from the **weathering** and **erosion** of pre-existing rocks, from biological activity (e.g. shells and organic matter) or from chemical precipitation (e.g. **evaporites**).

Sedimentary rocks: Formed from the **lithification** (cementation) of sediment. Sedimentary rocks may be composed of mineral or rock particles (**clasts**) to form sandstones and claystones or sediments, of biological origin to form limestone and peat, or of chemical precipitation to form **evaporites**.

Shale: A fine-grained sedimentary rock composed of clay particles that splits easily into thin layers.

Silica (silicate): Silicon dioxide. (Mineral consisting of or incorporating silica.)

Sill: A sheet-like body of **igneous** rock which, in general, does not cross-cut the layering of the rocks that it **intrudes**.

Silurian: The third **period** of the **Palaeozoic Era**, ranging from 445 to 395 million years ago.

Slate: A fine-grained **metamorphic** rock formed from **clays** and **shales**. The alignment of platy minerals during metamorphism enables the rock to be split easily along planar surfaces not necessarily parallel to the bedding within the original sediment.

Soil creep: Gradual movement of wet soil on a slope, moving under the influence of gravity.

Spit: An elongate deposit of sand or gravel projecting obliquely seawards from a shoreline.

SSSI: Site of Special Scientific Interest.

Stage: A **chronostratigraphic** (time-rock) unit.

Stegosaur: A **Jurassic/Cretaceous** quadrapedal dinosaur characterised by a double row of protective bony plates along its back.

Stomata: Minute pores in the surface of a leaf through which gas and vapour may pass.

Strata (Singular: **stratum**): Layers within **sedimentary** rocks. The term is often used instead of **beds**.

Stratigraphical unit: A body of rock defined by its **lithological** features (**lithostratigraphical** unit) or **fossil** content (**biostratigraphical** unit).

Stratigraphy: The study of rock **strata** and their distribution in space and time.

Stratotype (type section): A seqence of **sedimentary** rocks at a particular locality chosen as the standard against which other sequences can be compared. Stratotypes are established for lithostratigraphical and biostratigraphical units, both regionally and internationally. *See* **stratigraphical unit**.

Stromatolite: A laminated mounded structure composed of limestone built by **cyano-bacteria**. Stromatolites form today in warm shallow tropical seas. They appear in the early **Precambrian**.

Subduction: Process whereby one plate made up of **oceanic crust** is carried down into the **mantle** beneath another **plate**.

Superglacial (Sometimes, 'supraglacial'): Literally 'over' or 'upon' the ice. Thus superglacial deposits are those that accumulated on the ice surface. When the ice disappears they are left on the land surface, frequently forming hummocks of sand, gravel and clay.

Sustainability: The concept of meeting the needs of the present without compromising the ability of future generations to meet their needs. In nature conservation terms, it refers to the use of a natural resource in a way where it can be renewed, such that the environment's natural qualities are maintained.

Talus: The accumulation of rock fragments at the foot of a cliff. Also called scree.

Taxon (Plural: taxa): Any unit of classification of organisms (e.g. phylum, class, order, family, genus, species).

Tectonism (Adjective: tectonic): Deformation of the Earth's **crust** and the consequent structural effects (e.g. **faulting**, **folding** etc.).

Tertiary: The penultimate geological **period**, ranging from 65 to 1.6 million years ago.

Till: Synonymous with boulder clay.

Tombolo: A **bar** or **spit** of sand or shingle, linking an island to the mainland or another island.

(Marine) Transgression: An advance of the sea over land, due to movements of the Earth's **crust** or to a global rise in sea level.

Triassic: The first **period** of the **Mesozoic Era**, ranging from 230 to 195 million years ago.

Trilobite: An extinct class of marine **arthropods**.

Tuff: A **lithified** volcanic ash.

Type area/locality: The location where the type section (or **stratotype**) for a **stratigraphical unit** is located, or where the original type section or **fossil** was first described. For example, Kimmeridge Bay in Dorset is the type locality for the Kimmeridge Clay Formation (a lithostratigraphic unit).

Unconformity: The surface that separates two sedimentary sequences of different ages; it represents a gap in the geological record when there was erosion and/or no deposition. There is often an angular discordance between the two sequences.

Variscan Orogeny: A mountain-building episode that occurred during the late **Carboniferous Period** in south-west England, South Wales and southern Ireland.

Vascular tissue: Living matter made up of, or containing, vessels that convey blood or sap, which transport nutrients etc.

Vent: The opening within a volcano through which **igneous** material is ejected.

Volcanic rocks: **Lavas**, ashes and near-surface **igneous intrusions** associated with volcanoes.

Weathering: The process by which rocks are broken down in place by physical, chemical and biological processes.

Xenolith: A piece of pre-existing rock found within an **igneous** rock, often composed of pieces of **country rock** into which **magma** was **intruded**.

Index